Questions about this course

DEFINITION

1. **What is this support group?** This support group is an intentional face-to-face gathering of 3 to 12 people on a regular time schedule with the common purpose of discovering and growing in the possibilities of the abundant life in Christ.

OPEN

2. **Can a person who is on their way back to God be in this support group?** Yes. That is what this group is all about. This group is for:

   • People who may be hesitant about the church but want to revive their spiritual life.

   • People who are going through a dry spell in their spiritual life.

   • People who are dealing with personal struggles in their life.

   • People who are down on themselves and need encouragement to see beyond their own shortcomings.

   • People who are looking for hope in the face of seemingly insurmountable difficulties.

   • People who flashed across your mind as you read over this list.

FIRST SESSION

3. **What will we do at the first meeting?** Part of the "Orientation" session is to get acquainted and to decide on the Ground Rules for your group. To keep the first session from going too long, members should read the Preface on page 6 later, or have the leader make the Preface into a short talk.

THREE OPTIONS	4. **What do we study for the rest of the course?** Your group has three basic options: (See the schedule in the Table of Contents.)

- **Option One:** Track 1—Life Stories. A general discussion of the issue, including contemporary Life Stories.

- **Option Two:** Track 2—Bible Study. A study on the issue, comparing your experience to a story from Scripture.

- **Option Three:** Tracks 1 and 2 (for a total of 13 weeks rather than 7 weeks)—spending two sessions on each topic. If possible, we recommend that you choose this option so that your group can benefit from both Life Stories and Bible Study.

AGENDA	5. **What is the agenda for the sessions?** See page 2 for the three important parts to every group meeting. Page 2 also explains how to form groups of four for the Study segment of the meeting.
LENGTH OF SESSIONS	6. **How long is each small group session?** Sixty to 90 minutes, if you use the suggested times for each part of the session given in the book. You may have to pick and choose the questions that fit the needs and interests of the group.
LEADERSHIP	7. **Who leads the meetings?** Anyone may guide these discussions. The leader doesn't have to be a teacher or counselor, but simply gets the group started and keeps it on track. One person can lead all the time, or you can rotate leadership among the members.
WHAT THE GROUP IS	8. **What is at the heart of this group?** This is a support group. This is a group in which you can tell your stories. This is a group where you can learn together, pray together, laugh together, and, if necessary, cry together.
WHAT THE GROUP IS NOT	9. **What will NOT take place in this group?** This is not a therapy group. This is not a lecture by an expert. This is not group counseling. This is not a replacement for professional therapy.

STREAMS IN THE DESERT

SERENDIPITY EXECUTIVE EDITOR:
Lyman Coleman

AUTHOR:
Keith Madsen

CARTOONIST:
Christopher Werner

LAYOUT PRODUCTION TEAM:
Sharon Penington
Erika Tiepel

RELIEVING SPIRITUAL DRYNESS

TOPICS	SESSION	TRACK 1 LIFE STORIES	TRACK 2 BIBLE STUDY
ORIENTATION	1	Get Acquainted	
A TIME OF WRESTLING	2	Roy, Madeleine L'Engle	
	3		Genesis 32:22–30
INSUFFICIENT RESOURCES	4	Maya Angelou, Warren	
	5		Genesis 21:14–20
A DRY PAST AND FUTURE	6	Ben, Katrina	
	7		Ezekiel 37:1–14
FEELING LONELY	8	Paul, Marie	
	9		1 Kings 19:1–18
WAITING FOR GOD	10	Connie, Jerry	
	11		Exodus 32:1–14
MINISTERED TO BY ANGELS	12	Art, Lynette	
	13		Matthew 4:1–11

Serendipity House • P.O. Box 1012 • Littleton, CO 80160

TOLL FREE 1-800-525-9563

96 97 98 99 / **201S series•CHG** / 6 5 4 3 2

Beginning a Small Group

1. AGENDA: There are three parts to every group meeting.

GATHERING
15 min.
Purpose:
To break the ice

STUDY
30 min.
Purpose: To
discuss the issue

CARING
15–45 min.
Purpose: To share
your own needs

2. FEARLESS FOURSOME: If you have more than seven in your group at any time, call the option play when the time comes for Study, and subdivide into groups of 4 for greater participation. (In 4's, everyone will share and you can finish the Study in 30 minutes). Then regather the group for CARING.

GATHERING
All Together

STUDY
Groups of 4

CARING
Back Together

3. EMPTY CHAIR: Pull up an empty chair during CARING at the close and ask God to fill this chair each week. Remember, by breaking into groups of four for the Study time, you can grow numerically without feeling "too big" as a group.

The Group Leader needs an apprentice-in-training at all times so that the apprentice can start a new "cell" when the group size is 12 or more.

GROUND RULES

10. **What are the ground rules for the group?** You will have a chance to discuss expectations and ground rules during the first small group session on pages 14–15.

CONTINUING

11. **What happens to the group after finishing the course?** The group is free to disband or to continue. (See the fold-out description of the entire line of Serendipity small group materials in the center section of this book.) In Session 13, you will find various suggestions for continuing on as a group. Call Toll Free **1-800-525-9563** for suggestions about other courses and to receive a free Serendipity Resource Catalog.

PREFACE

In ancient times people used to think that the gods lived only on the mountaintops. It was demons and evil spirits who lived in the valleys. Thus the Greeks went to Mount Olympus to contact deity, and Native Americans of the Northwest found the divine centered on Mount Rainier ("Tahoma"), "the mountain that was god." Even in the Judaic-Christian tradition, Moses met God on Mount Sinai, worship centered on Mount Zion, and those who sought God would "lift up their eyes to the hills." In a sense this perspective still holds today. We want our spiritual lives to be lived solely on the "mountaintops"—filled with spiritual highs and moments of ecstasy and oneness with all of life. We don't want any valleys. We don't want any times in the desert, amidst its loneliness, dryness and desolation. We certainly don't think we can find God there.

The problem with focusing on the mountaintops of life is that very few of us live much of our lives there. Most of us spend far more time in the valleys. And occasionally we all find ourselves in a desert. To live in the desert is to feel life has gone dry on us. It is to look around and find that the things that nurture life—friends, meaning, direction, excitement—just aren't there to the degree we would like. In such times we may feel, like the ancients, that God isn't there in our desert either. It's not that we have stopped believing in God. It's just that somehow we don't feel his presence with us.

If you have found yourself in a desert, facing spiritual dryness, this course is for you. You will be sharing with others who know what it is like. But we will also focus on the importance of such times for our spiritual development, and how by using some classical spiritual disciplines we can find, as the psalmist found, that God is even with us "in the valley of the shadow of death."

In this course we will be looking at different aspects of what it means to experience "spiritual dryness," and with each aspect we will look at some disciplines which particularly apply to that area of need. These aspects of our experience include:

A Time of Wrestling
Spiritual dryness sometimes entails a struggle that we cannot clearly define. This often is the most difficult aspect of our dilemma. If we can define a problem or a crisis—a loved one who died, a marriage that is in stress, problems with our career—then we at least have a start toward a solution. But when our problem is more nebulous, so is the solution.

Sometimes we are wrestling in the area of assessing our overall life direction. Maya Angelou writes of such a wrestling: "Each of us has a right and the responsibility to assess the roads which lie ahead, and those over which we have traveled, and if the future road looms ominous or unpromising, and the road back uninviting, then we need to gather our resolve and, carrying only the necessary baggage, step off that road into another direction."[1]

Whatever it is we are wrestling with, a couple of spiritual disciplines that are especially helpful are solitude and meditation. Both help us get in touch with God and our self, and in so doing get a better grip on where we are and where we are going in life. Solitude is getting away from all of the distracting noisiness of our world, and meditation is releasing that same noisiness from our mind and spirit. Richard Foster, who has written much on the spiritual disciplines, writes, "If we hope to move beyond the superficialities of our culture—including our religious culture—we must be willing to go down into the recreating silences, into our inner world of contemplation."[2]

Having Insufficient Resources
Finding our self in a desert is most often characterized by feeling we are without the resources necessary for life. In a literal desert that means food, water and shelter. In a spiritual desert what we lack is support, direction, encouragement and hope, to name a few.

When we are in a spiritual desert and think we have to find the resources that we need on our own, we can panic. Our sense of inadequacy can overwhelm us. That is why this aspect of spiritual dryness is best countered by the discipline of prayer. Prayer puts us in touch with the infinite resources of God. But prayer isn't a magic wand that we wave to take away all our troubles. Prayer is an act of submission to God, and an openness to God coming into our life and changing us. Sometimes we find that the big reason we are in the desert in the first place is that there is an aspect of our life—a sin, an area where we are out of harmony with God and the life God created—which needs to be changed. We have a tendency to hide such areas from others and even from ourselves. But to relieve our spiritual dryness, that needs to change. Richard Foster writes, "... when we pray God slowly and graciously reveals to us our hiding places, and sets us free from them."[3]

A Dry Past and Future
Spiritual dryness doesn't always come from the present moment. Sometimes it's because our spiritual desert extends into the past and future. Perhaps something happened in the past, we feel guilty about it, and it still drains us of our spiritual energy. Or maybe, as we look into the future, we see nothing of promise, nothing that excites us about where we are going. Just like a literal desert has the tendency to grow and extend into more fertile areas around it, so today's spiritual dryness extends into both past and future.

Two disciplines help us to keep spiritual dryness from spreading from past to present and from present to future: confession and submission. Confession keeps our past wrongs from enslaving us through feelings of guilt. Confession can be done directly to God, or is often even more helpful if done with a trusted friend or spiritual advisor, who can then help us to be assured of God's forgiveness.

Submission is more important as we look to the future. Spiritual dryness often comes when we look to the future with anxiety. If things are going fairly well, we are afraid that "our luck will run out." If they are going poorly, we are afraid that things will get even worse. Only when we learn to trust our future to God and God's leading can this change. A well-loved saying is, "I don't know what the future holds, but I know who holds the future." That is the spirit we must have.

Feeling Lonely
Oftentimes spiritual dryness comes from feeling lonely or unconnected to the people around us. There is much in modern society that lends to this. With our highly-mobile culture, we frequently do not get to know the people around us before we have to move on. Neighbors today often do not know each other, unless they live in a small town. Sensational stories of crime have made us suspicious of the people around us, and so we build high fences and double and triple lock our doors. We watch our movies on our home VCR. Many shop via the shopping channel or the internet, and many even worship at home watching a TV preacher. No wonder so many feel isolated and alone!

Money is no antidote to this loneliness. Maya Angelou tells the story of her Aunt Tee. Aunt Tee was a black woman who worked as a live-in housekeeper for wealthy people. One couple she worked for ate their meals in silence and never seemed to have any friends over. After work her own friends would often come over and they would laugh and play cards. One night her employers came to the door of her live-in quarters as she laughed and played cards with her friends. She thought they had come to make some demand of her, and so their real request surprised her. They said, "We hear you and your friends laughing every Saturday night, and we'd just like to watch you. We don't want to bother you. We'll be quiet and just watch."[4] What a picture of loneliness! Yet to one degree or other, it is true of many in our world today.

If loneliness is an important part of our own spiritual dryness, then we especially need the disciplines of worship and celebration. We need to be together with other people sharing in the celebration of what God has given us in life.

Waiting for God
When we hit a time of spiritual dryness, two of the questions which often come to mind are, where is God in the midst of this? Has God forgotten about me? Many of the Psalms voice that fear. That reminds us that even people who are people of faith can go through times of spiritual dry-

ness when it seems God is far away. While many of the disciplines we talk of elsewhere can help with this need, here we want to add the discipline of "simplicity." There are many things in our world which compete for the place God holds in our life—material wealth, success, the adulation of people—and when we give God's place over to those things, God can seem very far away. It has been said that if God seems far away, we should ask the question, "Who moved?" Often we will find it was us. That is not to say that every time we feel far from God it is because we have put something else in his place. Sometimes it's just part of the human condition we must go through. But if we use the discipline of simplicity to keep other "gods" from taking God's place in our life, those times of feeling God as distant should be fewer and farther between.

Ministered to by Angels

Even Jesus experienced times of spiritual dryness, such as in his wilderness temptations and Gethsemane. But the temptation experience reminds us that in the midst of Jesus' time of spiritual dryness, God sent angels to minister to him. God will similarly send "angels" (God's messengers who sometimes come in the form of human beings) to support and minister to us. However, if we are to receive support, we must also give it. This is where the discipline of service becomes important. We serve as part of a serving community, where we all become "angels" to each other.

We are God's children, and God wants us to be close to him. Sometimes we must go through some spiritually dry times. But utilizing spiritual disciplines used by Christians through the centuries can help us get through those dry times, and use them for new growth. That is what this course is about.

NOTES:

[1]Maya Angelou, *Wouldn't Take Nothing for My Journey Now* (New York: Bantam Books, 1993), p. 24.
[2]Richard J. Foster, *Celebration of Discipline* (San Francisco: Harper & Row, 1978), p. 13.
[3]Ibid, p. 30.
[4]Angelou, pp. 62–64.

<table>
<tr><td>

SESSION
1

</td><td>

Orientation

</td></tr>
</table>

PURPOSE

To get acquainted, to share your expectations and to decide on the ground rules for your group.

AGENDA

 Gathering   Study   Caring

OPEN

 GATHERING / 15 Minutes / All Together

Leader: Give out name tags and have everyone introduce themselves. As everyone gives their names, jot down their name and phone number inside the front cover. Briefly, go over the "Questions about this course" on pages 3–5 and summarize the "Preface" on pages 6–9 in your own words. Then, ask everyone to turn to this page as you explain the 3-part agenda of each meeting: (1) Gathering—15 minutes; (2) Study—30 minutes, and (3) Caring—15–45 minutes. (If you have 90 minutes for the meeting, use the extra 30 minutes for Caring).

Start off by reading or asking for a volunteer to read the Introduction below. Then, use the Ice-Breaker to get acquainted.

INTRODUCTION

Welcome to this course we are calling *Streams in the Desert!* It is for people who are going through what can best be described as "spiritual dryness"—times when our spiritual life has hit a lull, and we just don't seem to be as personally "centered" or as close to God as we would like to be. In the next few weeks, you will have a chance to talk about issues related to your own spiritual life, and the times of "dryness" you have experienced. You will also get to know each other and learn to support one another.

Often we are under the impression that we should avoid "down" times at all costs. But sometimes it is just such times that show us something new about ourselves, or about our God. Richard Foster, who is well-known for his emphasis on spiritual disciplines, writes, "What is involved in entering the dark night of the soul? It may be a sense of dryness, depression, even lostness. It strips us of overdependence on the emotional life. The notion, often heard today, that such experiences can be avoided and that we should live in peace and comfort, joy and celebration, only betrays the fact that much contemporary experience is surface slush. The dark night is one of the ways God brings us to a hush, a stillness, so that He may work an inner transformation upon the soul."[1]

In this course you will have a chance to explore your own spiritual journey and the spiritual disciplines that lead to transformation.

You will have to decide which track you want to follow in this course. (See schedule in the Table of Contents.) Track 1 is an introductory track—with life stories taken from contemporary life. Track 2 is a deeper track—with case studies taken from stories in the Bible. If you can give 13 weeks to this course, you can take both tracks—Track 1 the first week, Track 2 the next week.

In this first session, be sure to set aside at least 30 minutes at the close to make these decisions. Now, start with the Ice-Breaker. Call time after 15 minutes and move on to the Study.

Ice-Breaker. Use the questions below to get acquainted. Go around the group on the first question. If you have time left over go around on the next question.

1. Begin by sharing your name, where you were raised, and who is in your "family" (this can mean biological family or the friends who are like family to you).

2. If you were to compare your family to a family in a TV show or movie, which one would you compare it to?
   - ❐ Leave It to Beaver
   - ❐ The Simpsons
   - ❐ The Cosby Show
   - ❐ Father Knows Best
   - ❐ Home Improvement
   - ❐ Roseanne
   - ❐ The Waltons
   - ❐ The Addams Family
   - ❐ Married With Children
   - ❐ Home Alone
   - ❐ The Rocky Horror Picture Show

STUDY / 30 Minutes / Groups of 4

Leader: If you have more than 7 in your group, we recommend that you move quickly into groups of 4 for this Study time (4 at the dining table, 4 at the kitchen table, etc.). In groups of 4, everyone can participate, and you can finish the Study in 30 minutes. Then, bring the entire group back together for the Caring time.

Life Stories. Have someone read out loud the stories of the two people below. Then discuss the questions which follow.

Shannon
Shannon was somewhat embarrassed as she tried to talk to her pastor. She had requested some counseling time in his office, but now that she was there, she was having difficulty explaining exactly what the problem was. Finally she found the words: she assured him that she believed in God, but somehow her relationship with him was not all she thought it should be. She saw other people who seemed excited about their faith, and heard people testify of how much God had done for them. In all hon-

esty, she felt that she had gotten where she was on her own. She rarely felt any sense of God's presence, and her prayers, when she said them, often seemed somewhat empty. She wondered what was wrong and what she should do.

Monty

Monty has been an active church-attender all of his life. For much of that time he has sung in the choir, and that has been the most important part of his spiritual life. An emotionally-expressive person, Monty has put all of himself into his songs. But recently there just hasn't been anything there. He began to feel like a fake when he sang, and on occasion he felt like crying during the song he was singing, even though the song was not a sad one. Finally he quit the choir, and just sat in the congregation. But even then the minister's sermons seemed empty to him. He said he felt driven, almost as if by demons, away from his church home.

DISCUSS

Questions:

1. When you were a child in grade school, which of the following was your view of God most like?
   - ❐ a stern, bearded man carrying lightning bolts
   - ❐ a grandfatherly type, like Santa Claus
   - ❐ like Jesus—God and Jesus were the same to me
   - ❐ a spirit—like Casper the Friendly Ghost!
   - ❐ I don't remember having a view of God.

"No one is surprised, though we sometimes complain, when faithful church members do not grow to maturity in Christ. With steady regularity we fail to realize the 'abundance of life' the gospel clearly promises."
—Dallas Willard in *The Spirit of the Disciplines*

2. Which part of the people's stories above sounds most like your own experience?
   - ❐ like Shannon—feeling my relationship with God is not all it should be
   - ❐ like Shannon—feeling like other people are more excited about their faith than I am
   - ❐ like Shannon—not really feeling like God has helped me that much
   - ❐ like Monty—feeling the songs of faith I sing are empty
   - ❐ like Monty—feeling weepy for no apparent reason
   - ❐ like Monty—feeling like the sermons I hear are empty
   - ❐ like Monty—feeling driven away from the church

3. If we are to talk in terms of "the dark night of the soul," how dark do you feel your spiritual life is right now?
   - ❐ not really dark—maybe like a hazy day
   - ❐ like an overcast day
   - ❐ like dusk, with a little daylight still in the sky
   - ❐ like night—but with a full moon
   - ❐ like a dark, overcast night, where not even lightning brightens the sky

4. How do you react to Richard Foster's idea stated in the Introduction to this session, "The dark night is one of the ways God brings us to a hush, a stillness, so that He may work an inner transformation upon the soul"?
   ❒ But I was happy like I was!
   ❒ I wouldn't describe my spiritual dryness as "a dark night."
   ❒ My dark night has lasted long enough for him to transform me several times over!
   ❒ I just don't see this heading in a positive direction.
   ❒ If there is hope at the end of this, maybe I can take it!
   ❒ other _____

5. How are you feeling right now about sharing your experience of spiritual dryness with the others in this group?
   ❒ I am not really the "sharing" type.
   ❒ I feel a little guilty and ashamed.
   ❒ If this will help, I'm ready.
   ❒ I'm not sure.

CARING / 15–45 Minutes / All Together

Leader: Bring all of the groups back together for a time of caring. In this first session, you need to set the ground rules and goals for your group. Then close the meeting together with the Serenity Prayer.

INTRODUCTION

Now is the time to decide what you want to get out of this course. For yourself. For your group. And to agree on the ground rules for your group. Follow these steps.

Step One: EXPECTATIONS. Give everyone a chance to share two things that you would like to get out of this course and this group, starting with the following list:

❒ to see what the Bible says about spiritual dryness
❒ to be in a small group where I can deal with spiritual dryness
❒ to get to know some other people who are dealing with spiritual dryness
❒ to learn how to pray
❒ to evaluate my spiritual journey
❒ to look at my lifestyle and the causes of dryness
❒ to reach out to others in my church
❒ other_____

GROUND RULES | **Step Two: GROUND RULES.** What are some ground rules you would like to set for this group? See if you can agree on two or three.

❑ ATTENDANCE: Group members will give priority to the group meetings for 13 weeks or sessions unless you decide on using only Track 1 or 2. (See schedule in the Table of Contents.)

❑ QUESTIONS ENCOURAGED: This is a support group for people who are struggling with all sorts of questions, including questions about your spiritual faith. Honest questions are encouraged.

❑ MISSION: This group will be "open" to anyone who is struggling, and also to anyone who is seeking or who is starting over in the Christian life ... and it will be the mission of this group to invite new people to the sessions.

❑ ACCOUNTABILITY: This group will be a support group. Prayer requests will be shared at the end of every session and group members will be encouraged to call each other to ask, "How's it going?"

❑ ADVICE-GIVING: It is okay to offer advice to another group member, but only when it is requested.

❑ CONFIDENTIALITY: Anything that is said in the group is kept in confidence.

❑ COVENANT: At the end of this course, the group will evaluate the experience and decide if they wish to continue as a group.

PRAYER | **Step Three: SERENITY PRAYER.** Close your time by reading this prayer together:

> *"Dear God, Grant us the serenity to accept the things that we cannot control, the courage to change the things we can, and the wisdom to know the difference. Amen."*

REMINDER | If you know of someone who would benefit from this course, now is the time to invite them. Next session you will start on the first issue in this course. It would be quite easy for a new person to join your group next session.

HOMEWORK | Ask everyone to read the Preface on pages 6–9 before the next session.

DIRECTORY | If you have not already jotted down their names, pass around your books and have everyone write their names and phone numbers in the GROUP DIRECTORY inside the front cover.

NOTE:

[1]Richard J. Foster, *Celebration of Discipline* (San Francisco: Harper & Row, 1978), p. 90.

A Time of Wrestling

| LIFE STORIES | BIBLE STUDY |

PURPOSE

To introduce the subject of "A Time of Wrestling" and to continue the process of becoming a group.

AGENDA

 Gathering Study Caring

OPEN

 GATHERING / 15 Minutes / All Together

Leader: Welcome any newcomers and explain the purpose of the course, the "ground rules" that you agreed upon in the last session and the three-part agenda for the meetings. Also, explain that this session is the first of two sessions on the issue of "A Time of Wrestling."

Start off by reading the Introduction to the group or ask for a volunteer to read it. Then, use the Ice-Breaker to start the meeting. Remember to keep to the 3-part agenda.

INTRODUCTION

Oftentimes a person who has been plagued by an unknown physical ailment will actually feel relieved when a diagnosis is discovered, even if the diagnosis is a serious disease. The reason is that they at least know what they are dealing with. Oftentimes a spiritual malaise can be the same way. We can't point to any one thing that is especially wrong, but rather than helping us feel better, that fact makes us feel worse. If we had just had something horrible happen, then at least we would have an excuse! Instead of falling off a cliff, we have just descended gradually into an abyss, from which we can find no way out. We may identify with a young ordained minister who called Christian author Keith Miller one time. He asked Keith, "... what happens when a person makes a conscious attempt to commit his entire life to the living God, lives a few joyous, productive years in his church—maybe even becomes an ordained minister—and then wakes up one day and finds that the well has gone dry. 'Faith' has become only a word again."[1]

Part of our response to people like this young minister needs to be "Hey, there are others like you! Let's share and learn from each other!" But part of what we must realize also is that we have made our spiritual lives dependent on feelings, which as a matter of course ebb and flow. What we need to do is to discipline ourselves in ways that will maintain our relationship to God even when the feelings aren't there.

Two important disciplines in helping us with our times of unfocused wrestling are the disciplines of solitude and meditation. Solitude is getting away from the confusion and pressures of the modern world to get in touch with ourselves and our God. Part of the reason we sometimes don't know why life has turned dry is that we have lost touch with ourselves. We have spent so much time attending to demands of others that we have ignored our inner voice. Solitude can help remedy that. Richard Foster suggests utilizing the "little solitudes" that come naturally to life, like the time commuting to work, or that time at night before going to sleep. But he also advises finding a quiet place to go to on a regular basis, and even, if we can afford it, building a special quiet place into our home.[2] Meditation is using that solitude to push out the thoughts of the day, and focus on God. There is a difference between Christian meditation and its Eastern counterpart. In Eastern meditation the aim is simply to empty the mind, whereas in Christian meditation, it is to empty it in order to fill it—fill it with God's presence and God's thoughts.

This is the first of two sessions where we will explore the issues of using solitude and meditation in response to our wrestling. In this session, the emphasis will be on sharing your own story. If you wish to spend another session on this topic and go deeper into this issue, you can move to Track 2 ... or you can stay in Track 1 and go to the next issue. This session has the same three-part agenda as the last session.

Ice-Breaker. Go around on question #1, letting everyone share their answer, and then do the same with question #2.

1. Choose five of the following pairs and tell which of the pair says best where you are most likely to be found. Are you more likely to be found ...

    at McDonald's . . . . at Chez Pierre's
    at K-Mart . . . . at Saks Fifth Avenue
    at a ballgame. . . . . at a concert
    at a friend's having coffee . . . . at work, making deals
    seeking sand and surf . . . . surfing the Internet
    finding new places . . . . returning to old places
    at a children's program . . . . at a board meeting
    tending livestock . . . . in the stock market

2. If you are wanting not to be found, where do you go?

STUDY / 30 Minutes / Groups of 4

Leader: If you have more than 7 in your group, we recommend that you move quickly into groups of 4 for the Study time (4 at the dining table, 4 at the kitchen table, etc.). In groups of 4, everyone can participate and you can finish the Study in 30 minutes. Then, bring the entire group back together for the Caring time.

Life Stories. Have someone read out loud the stories of the two people below. Then, use the questions to share some of your own experience.

Roy

Roy didn't know what to think when his church proposed a 24-hour retreat of silence. He is a social, active person who starts to get down whenever he doesn't have enough to do. This retreat would be at a monastery, and he would have to be in a small simple room, without any work projects or even a television set. The only time he would be able to leave would be for an occasional 30-minute instructional session on meditation. Still, Roy was curious about the experience, and so he went. During his time of silence he found himself reading his Bible in a new way. He started reading it like he had back in 7th grade when he first became a Christian—he read it for direction for how he should live his life, instead of to find answers for theological dilemmas. Following the advice of one of the spiritual advisors, he also meditated on a series of words, including "judgment" and "belonging." He realized that he constantly felt like he didn't belong, and that he had to prove himself to people who were standing in judgment of him. He worked constantly in order to prove himself. He hated to relax and just enjoy himself because he felt people would judge him as lazy and unproductive. His scriptural study underlined that he needed to look to please God instead of pleasing people. As he meditated on God's acceptance of him, he felt tears forming in his eyes, which was something he hardly ever allowed to happen. By the time the retreat was over, Roy didn't want to leave.

Madeleine L'Engle

Author Madeleine L'Engle (not a pseudonym) writes of where she goes for solitude: "... often I need to get away completely, if only for a few minutes. My special place is a small brook in a green glade, a circle of quiet from which there is no visible sign of human beings. There's a natural stone bridge over the brook, and I sit there, dangling my legs and looking through the foliage at the sky reflected in the water, and things slowly come back into perspective ... The brook wanders through a tunnel of foliage, and the birds sing more sweetly there than anywhere else; or perhaps it is just that when I am at the brook I have time to be aware of them, and I move slowly into a kind of peace that is marvelous, 'annihilating all that's made to a green thought in a green shade.' If I sit for a while, then my impatience, crossness, frustration, are indeed annihilated, and my sense of humor returns."[3]

DISCUSS **Questions:**

1. Madeleine L'Engle speaks of a special place where she spends time. What special place did you go to as a child when you wanted to get away from your parents and/or brothers and sisters?

2. What aspects of the stories above do you relate to most strongly?
   - ❐ Like Roy, I get anxious when I don't have enough to do.
   - ❐ Like Roy, I prayed and read my Bible more when I was a youth.
   - ❐ Like Roy, I often feel like I don't belong.
   - ❐ Like Roy, I often feel like people are standing in judgment of me.
   - ❐ Like Roy, I have difficulty relaxing.
   - ❐ Like Madeleine L'Engle, nature pacifies me.
   - ❐ Like Madeleine L'Engle, I feel the need to get away at times.

3. If the young minister in the Introduction had called you, what do you think you would have told him? What experience could you have shared that was like his?

4. In the Introduction it is said, "Part of the reason we sometimes don't know why life has turned dry is that we have lost touch with ourselves." Do you agree? Why or why not?

5. Of the various ways of finding solitude, which do you most need to emphasize more in your life?
   - ❐ utilizing the "little solitudes" of life, like my commuting time, to meditate
   - ❐ reserving a "private place" to get away to in my home
   - ❐ finding a "circle of quiet" in nature like Madeleine L'Engle
   - ❐ going on a 24-hour "silent retreat" like Roy
   - ❐ other _____

6. In the Introduction it is said that Christian meditation differs from Eastern meditation in that in Christian meditation one doesn't just empty the mind—one must also fill it with God's presence and God's thoughts. In all honesty, how do you think such a discipline might affect your own spiritual dryness?
   - ❐ I think I'd get more out of just emptying my mind.
   - ❐ Thinking of God makes me feel guilty, which makes me anxious!
   - ❐ I wouldn't know *how* to focus my mind on God.
   - ❐ Maybe if I had someone encouraging and helping me, like Roy.
   - ❐ This is exactly what I need in my life!

 CARING / 15–45 Minutes / All Together

Leader: Regather all the groups for the Caring time. Start off with Sharing. Then, if you feel comfortable, share prayer requests.

SHARING

Which scriptural promise brings you the most meaning as you deal with spiritual dryness? Pick one and tell the group why you chose the one you did.

Blessed is the man who does not walk in the counsel of the wicked or stand in the way of sinners or sit in the seat of mockers. But his delight is in the law of the Lord, and on his law he meditates day and night. He is like a tree planted by streams of water, which yields its fruit in season and whose leaf does not wither. Whatever he does prospers.   *Psalm 1:1–3*

Cast your cares on the Lord and he will sustain you; he will never let the righteous fall.   *Psalm 55:22*

And God is able to make all grace abound to you, so that in all things at all times, having all that you need, you will abound in every good work.   *2 Corinthians 9:8*

Ask and it will be given to you; seek and you will find; knock and the door will be opened to you.   *Matthew 7:7*

I can do everything through him who gives me strength.   *Philippians 4:13*

And we know that in all things God works for the good of those who love him, who have been called according to his purpose.   *Romans 8:28*

"You will go out in joy and be led forth in peace; the mountains and hills will burst into song before you, and all the trees of the field will clap their hands. Instead of the thornbush will grow the pine tree, and instead of briers the myrtle will grow. This will be for the Lord's renown, for an everlasting sign, which will not be destroyed."   *Isaiah 55:12–13*

PRAYER

Have group members answer the question,

"How can we help you in prayer this week?"

The leader will close the group in prayer, remembering the concerns each person shared. If you would like to pray for other group members during the week, write down the prayer requests so you can remember them.

REMINDER

If you know of someone who would benefit from this course, now is the time to invite them. It would be quite easy for a new person to join your group next session.

NOTES:

[1]Keith Miller, *A Second Touch* (Waco, TX: Word Books, 1967), p. 21.
[2]Richard J. Foster, *Celebration of Discipline* (San Francisco: Harper & Row, 1978), p. 93.
[3]Madeleine L'Engle, *A Circle of Quiet* (New York: Farrar, Straus and Giroux, 1972), p. 4.

A Time of Wrestling

LIFE STORIES	BIBLE STUDY

PURPOSE

To go deeper into the subject of "A Time of Wrestling" and to share your own experience through a Bible Story about this issue.

AGENDA

 Gathering Study Caring

OPEN

 GATHERING / 15 Minutes / All Together

Leader: Welcome any newcomers and explain the purpose of the group, the "ground rules" that you have agreed upon and the three-part agenda for the meetings. Explain that this session is the second of the two on the issue of "A Time of Wrestling."

The purpose of the Gathering time is to break the ice. Call time after 15 minutes and move on.

Ice-Breaker: The Old Neighborhood. Go around on question 1 and let everyone share their "old neighborhood." If you have time left over, go around again on question 2.

1. Was your "old neighborhood" more like ...
   - ❏ Sesame Street—urban and multi-cultural
   - ❏ Bill Cosby's neighborhood—distinctively ethnic
   - ❏ Leave it to Beaver—suburban housing with a common cultural background
   - ❏ The Waltons—rural and spread out, but close-knit

2. Choose as many of the following to share as you have time for:
   - Where did the kids gather in your neighborhood?
   - What were your favorite activities to do together?
   - Where were the special places—the best climbing trees, the best fishing holes? The places you could go to hide from adults?
   - Where were the "danger spots"—the yards with mean dogs, the "Oscar the Grouches" who didn't seem to like people, the "haunted" houses?
   - Who were some kids you remember as having really distinctive things about them—the "Weird Harolds" and "Fat Alberts"?

STUDY / 30 Minutes / Groups of 4

Leader: If you have more than 7 in your group, we recommend that you subdivide into groups of 4 for this Study, so that you can finish the Study in 30 minutes and everyone can participate.

INTRODUCTION

Wrestling With God. In the following story Jacob is heading back to his "old neighborhood," which was also the land God had promised him and his descendants as the place for their future. On the way he wrestles alone with a man who ends up being not a man at all, but an angel of God. For an Israelite that was the equivalent of encountering God himself. Jacob is wounded in the midst of this wrestling, which becomes a pivotal experience in his life, because it serves to clarify his life purpose, and gives him a new identity (the name "Israel" means "he struggles with God.") Many of us have to go through a similar time when we "wrestle" with God. As you look at the following story, think of what the nature is of your own "wrestling with God."

Have someone in your group read out loud the following Scripture. Then go around on the first question and let everyone speak up. Then, go around again on the next question, etc. Be sure to save the last 15–45 minutes for the Caring time.

²²That night Jacob got up and took his two wives, his two maidservants and his eleven sons and crossed the ford of the Jabbok. ²³After he had sent them across the stream, he sent over all his possessions. ²⁴So Jacob was left alone, and a man wrestled with him till daybreak. ²⁵When the man saw that he could not overpower him, he touched the socket of Jacob's hip so that his hip was wrenched as he wrestled with the man. ²⁶Then the man said, "Let me go, for it is daybreak."

But Jacob replied, "I will not let you go unless you bless me."

²⁷The man asked him, "What is your name?"

"Jacob," he answered.

²⁸Then the man said, "Your name will no longer be Jacob, but Israel, because you have struggled with God and with men and have overcome."

²⁹Jacob said, "Please tell me your name."

But he replied, "Why do you ask my name?" Then he blessed him there.

³⁰So Jacob called the place Peniel, saying, "It is because I saw God face to face, and yet my life was spared."

Genesis 32:22–30

1. Jacob encountered God in this unusual way during a period of aloneness. Where do you go to find time alone?
   - ❏ Good question—I don't!
   - ❏ I go in the "john" and lock the door!
   - ❏ I go out driving.
   - ❏ I go to my office.
   - ❏ I have this special little place out in nature.
   - ❏ I'm alone most of the time.
   - ❏ other _____

2. How do you relate to your times of aloneness?
    - ❏ I avoid them—I crave people!
    - ❏ When I'm alone I feel lonely.
    - ❏ I go right to the TV.
    - ❏ I use them to get things done.
    - ❏ I use them to reflect or meditate.
    - ❏ I use them to read or listen to music.

3. In Jacob's wrestling, he seemed unclear who he was wrestling with—a man or an angel of God. In what way is your own wrestling with God related to wrestling with others in your human relationships?

4. In your wrestling match with God right now, how do you see the match going?
    - ❏ He's got me in a "headlock."
    - ❏ He's lifted me above his head and is spinning me in circles!—I don't know which way is up!
    - ❏ I think he's got me pinned!
    - ❏ We're countering each other's moves, and I think this match may well last to "daybreak"!
    - ❏ I'm fighting free from his grasp.
    - ❏ I've "thrown the match"—I was rooting for him anyway!

5. What "wound" have you received which hinders your search for spiritual wholeness?
    - ❏ The wound of guilt—It won't go away.
    - ❏ The wound of cynicism—I'm having a hard time trusting again.
    - ❏ The wound of despair—I don't know if I can hope.
    - ❏ The wound of broken relationship—I feel alienated and alone.
    - ❏ The wound of a fractured self-image—I can't believe God would love me.

6. What blessing do you need from God to help you find healing?
    - ❏ assurance of his forgiveness
    - ❏ some indication that he really cares
    - ❏ direction to help put my life back together
    - ❏ courage to help me face myself honestly
    - ❏ faith to believe his promises

7. How do you now see the disciplines of solitude and meditation helping you to receive this blessing?

CARING / 15–45 Minutes / All Together

Leader: Regather all the groups for the Caring time. Start off with sharing. Then, if you feel comfortable, move into a time of prayer.

SHARING

King David experienced times of feeling distant from God. As the following psalm expresses, David at one point felt forgotten by God, even though deep down he knew God was with him. Read these excerpts from Psalm 42 together as a litany, breaking the group in half. Or choose two volunteers to alternate reading.

Reader(s) 1:
As the deer pants for streams of water,
so my soul pants for you, O God.
My soul thirsts for God, for the living God.
When can I go and meet with God?

Reader(s) 2:
My tears have been my food day and night,
while men say to me all day long,
"Where is your God?"
These things I remember as I pour out my soul:
how I used to go with the multitude,
leading the procession to the house of God,
with shouts of joy and thanksgiving
among the festive throng.

Reader(s) 1:
Why are you downcast, O my soul:
Why so disturbed within me? Put your hope in God,
for I will yet praise him, my Savior and my God.

Reader(s) 2:
Deep calls to deep in the roar of your waters;
all your waves and breakers have swept over me.
By day the Lord directs his love,
at night his song is with me—
a prayer to the God of my life.

Reader(s) 1:
I say to God my Rock, "Why have you forgotten me?
Why must I go about mourning,
oppressed by the enemy?"

Reader(s) 2:
Why are you downcast, O my soul?
Why so disturbed within me?
Put your hope in God, for I will yet praise him,
my Savior and my God.

PRAYER

Take time to share prayer requests. Then close with a time of prayer, remembering the requests that have been shared and the experiences of wrestling and woundedness that were shared earlier in the session. If you would like to pray in silence, say the word "Amen" when you have finished your prayer, so that the next person will know when to start.

Insufficient Resources

LIFE STORIES	BIBLE STUDY

PURPOSE

To introduce the subject of "Insufficient Resources" and to share your own life stories.

AGENDA

 Gathering Study Caring

OPEN

 GATHERING / 15 Minutes / All Together

Leader: Welcome any newcomers and explain the purpose of the group, the "ground rules" and the three-part agenda of the meeting. Also, explain that this session is the first of two sessions on the subject of "Insufficient Resources." For more background on this topic, refer back to the Preface on page 7.

Start off by reading the Introduction to the group or ask for a volunteer to read it. Then, use the Ice-Breaker to start the meeting. Remember to stick to the time limits in the 3-part agenda.

INTRODUCTION

How most of us look at a difficult situation depends largely on the resources we see ourselves as having to face that situation. If we feel confident in our resources, then a difficult situation is nothing more than a challenge—a challenge of the sort that often makes life more exciting. But when we face a physical or spiritual dilemma and feel ourselves to be without sufficient resources to handle it, then the dilemma can drag us down. When we go through a spiritual down time, a spiritual desert, the most notable resources we lack are support, encouragement, direction and hope. The discipline of prayer helps bring these to us. It brings them to us when we pray for them directly, but even when we are praying for the needs of others as well. Dallas Willard points out, "Even when we are praying for or about things other than our own spiritual needs and growth, the effect of conversing with God cannot fail to have a pervasive and spiritually strengthening effect on all aspects of our personality."[1] Perhaps the reason it does this is that it helps us to feel more connected to God and others.

We will have two sessions on the discipline of prayer as a response to our feeling that we have "insufficient resources," and this is the first. In this session, the emphasis will be on sharing your own story. If you wish to spend another session on this topic and go deeper into this issue, you can choose to move to Track 2 for the next session ... or you can stay in Track 1 and move to the next issue. This session has the same three-part agenda as the last session. To get started, use the Ice-Breaker below.

Ice-Breaker: Life Signs. Go around on question 1 and let everyone share. Then go around again on question 2.

1. If you were to select a traffic sign to tell how you've been seeking to live your life, what sign would it be?
   - ❏ "Merge"—because I've been trying to get along with everyone
   - ❏ "Slow"—because I've been seeking to slow down and experience more of life
   - ❏ "Keep Right"—because I'm trying to keep my life on the right track
   - ❏ "No U-Turn"—because I'm resisting the urge to go back to the past
   - ❏ "One Way"—because I'm seeking to be more decisive in my life direction
   - ❏ "Yield"—because I'm seeking to yield my life to God
   - ❏ "Children Playing"—because I'm trying to let out the "child" in me
   - ❏ "Under Construction"—because I'm changing so much

2. If God were to give you a "traffic ticket" right now for how you are living your life, what would it be for?
   - ❏ "Speeding"—not slowing down enough to really live
   - ❏ "Failing to yield"—trying to do things my own way
   - ❏ "Blocking traffic"—I feel I've been getting in the way of others who are doing more.
   - ❏ "Illegal U-turn"—I have been trying to live in the past.
   - ❏ "Driving the wrong way on a one-way street"—I need to turn my life around.

STUDY / 30 Minutes / Groups of 4

Leader: Remember, the Study in the first session on each issue (Track 1) is based on Life Stories. If there are 7 or more in your group, quickly subdivide into groups of 4 so that everyone can participate, and you can finish the Study in 30 minutes. Then, call the entire group back together at the close.

Life Stories. Have someone read out loud the stories of the two people on the next page. Then, use the questions to share some of your own experience.

Maya Angelou

Author Maya Angelou (not a pseudonym) tells how she learned that God would give her the resources she needed for hard times. She writes of her grandmother: "One of my earliest memories of Mamma, of my grand-mother, is a glimpse of a tall cinnamon-colored woman with a deep, soft voice, standing thousands of feet up in the air on nothing visible. That incredible vision was a result of what my imagination would do each time Mamma drew herself up to her full six feet, clasped her hands behind her back, looked up into a distant sky, and said, 'I will step out on the word of God.' The depression, which was difficult for everyone, especially so for a single black woman in the South tending her crippled son and two grandchildren, caused her to make the statement of faith often. She would look up as if she could see herself into the heavens, and tell her family in particular and the world in general, 'I will step out on the word of God.' Immediately I could see her flung into space, moons at her feet and stars at her head, comets swirling around her. Naturally, since Mamma stood out on the word of God, and Mamma was over six feet tall, it wasn't difficult for me to have faith. I grew up knowing that the word of God had power."[2]

Warren

Warren had always tried to teach his children a strong faith in God. But there came a time when it was difficult for him to feel and proclaim that faith. He had recently moved his family to a new community. But for over a year after the move they were unable to sell their house in the old com-munity. Paying for two houses was making the bills mount up fast, and soon he found himself confronted with bankruptcy. Many times he prayed to have the financial burden removed, but it just kept mounting up. God seemed very far away. One day he couldn't even manage to say the mealtime prayer for his family. One of his sons, however, stepped in and said it for him. He prayed for strength for his father in the midst of their ordeal.

DISCUSS

Questions:

1. Maya Angelou remembered back to the effect of the depression on her family, and her grandmother's response to it. What crisis or stress do you remember your childhood family having to weather? What family member took the lead in pulling the family through?

2. Both Maya Angelou's "Mamma" and Warren's family went through crisis times, when they wondered if they had the resources to manage, and they reacted in different ways. Place an "X" on the following continuum according to whether the way you find your-self is closer to "Mamma" or Warren:

LIKE WARREN _____LIKE MAMMA
Not even able to pray   **Stepping out on the Word of God**

3. The Introduction mentions four resources people often feel they are short of during a spiritually dry time. On the scales below, mark how you see yourself doing with each of those four resources:

SUPPORT

1	2	3	4	5
An "Empty Tank"				A "Full Tank"

ENCOURAGEMENT

1	2	3	4	5
An "Empty Tank"				A "Full Tank"

DIRECTION

1	2	3	4	5
An "Empty Tank"				A "Full Tank"

HOPE

1	2	3	4	5
An "Empty Tank"				A "Full Tank"

4. In the Introduction, Dallas Willard is quoted as saying, "Even when we are praying for or about things other than our own spiritual needs and growth, the effect of conversing with God cannot fail to have a pervasive and spiritually strengthening effect on all aspects of our personality." Do you agree? If so, give an example of when it has been true for you.

5. Rank the following aspects of a prayer life according to how important you see them being in counteracting spiritual dryness:
   ____ reserving a time for prayer each day
   ____ praying in the midst of life activities
   ____ praying for others as well as for myself
   ____ reserving part of my prayer time to listen to God
   ____ reserving part of my prayer time to praise and thank God
   ____ praying with family and loved ones
   ____ praying for specific needs instead of using generalities
   ____ sharing our true selves with God instead of trying to hide

6. Which of the aspects of prayer listed in question #5 do you need most to work on in your prayer life?

CARING / 15–45 Minutes / All Together

Leader: Bring all the groups back together for the Caring time. Start off the sharing by asking for prayer requests. Then, if you are comfortable, ask people to take these requests to God in a time of prayer.

SHARING

Take a few moments to reflect on this passage from Scripture before moving into prayer. The Scripture passage comes at a time in the life of God's people when they were almost hopelessly defeated.

Have one person read the passage aloud. Then go around and let each person share what God has said to them from this passage about their own situation.

> *"This is what the Lord says to you: 'Do not be afraid or discouraged because of this vast army. For the battle is not yours, but God's. ... You will not have to fight this battle. Take up your positions; stand firm and see the deliverance the Lord will give you, O Judah and Jerusalem. Do not be afraid; do not be discouraged. Go out and face them tomorrow, and the Lord will be with you.'"*
> *2 Chronicles 20:15b–17*

PRAYER

Now move into a time of prayer, remembering what others have shared regarding their struggles with spiritual dryness, insufficient resources or maintaining a meaningful prayer life.

Consider voicing a brief "sentence prayer." Each time a member of the group prays, the entire group responds in unison, *"Lord, hear our prayer."*

NOTES:

[1]Dallas Willard, *The Spirit of the Disciplines* (San Francisco: Harper & Row, 1988), p. 184.
[2]Maya Angelou, *Wouldn't Take Nothing for My Journey Now* (New York: Bantam Books, 1994), p. 74.

Insufficient Resources

LIFE STORIES	BIBLE STUDY

PURPOSE To go deeper into the subject of "Insufficient Resources" and to relate your experience to a story in the Bible.

AGENDA   Gathering   Study   Caring

OPEN

 GATHERING / 15 Minutes / All Together

Leader: Welcome any newcomers and explain the purpose of the group, the "ground rules" and the three-part agenda of the meetings. Explain that this session is the second of two on the subject of "Insufficient Resources."

The purpose of the Gathering time is to break the ice. Call time after 15 minutes and move on.

Ice-Breaker: Music in My Life. Put an "X" on each of the lines below— somewhere between the two extremes—to indicate how you are feeling right now about each area of your life. If time is limited, choose only two or three:

1. In my personal life, I'm feeling like ...
    Blues in the Night _____ Feeling Groovy

2. In my family life, I'm feeling like ...
    Stormy Weather _____ The Sound of Music

3. In my emotional life, I'm feeling like ...
    The Feeling Is Gone _____ On Eagle's Wings

4. In my work, school or career, I'm feeling like ...
    Take This Job _____ The Future's So Bright,
    and Shove it   I Gotta Wear 'Shades'!

5. In my spiritual life, I'm feeling like ...
    Sounds of Silence _____ Hallelujah Chorus

6. In my close relationships, I'm feeling like ...
    Love Is a Battlefield _____ You Light Up My Life

7. As I look at my immediate future, I'm feeling like ...
    Yesterday _____ To Dream the Impossible Dream

STUDY / 30 Minutes / Groups of 4

Leader: If you have more than 7 in your group, we recommend subdividing into groups of 4 (4 at the dining table, 4 at the kitchen table, etc.) so that you can finish the Study in 30 minutes and everyone can participate.

INTRODUCTION

A Single Mom, High and Dry. The following is the story of a single mom who was left high and dry in a real desert, because of lack of enough resources. But you don't have to be a single mom to have a similar experience. In the story, Abraham had taken Hagar as his second wife because his first wife, Sarah, had been barren. Hagar had a son named Ishmael. But then Sarah got pregnant in her old age and had a son named Isaac. Sarah became jealous of Hagar and her son, and had Abraham send her and her son away, which was the equivalent of divorce. Our passage picks up just as Abraham is sending Hagar away.

Have someone in your group read the story out loud. Then, go around on the first question and let everyone speak up. Then, go around again on the next question, etc. Remember, there are no right or wrong answers, so you don't have to feel intimidated by one who is more familiar with the Bible. Be sure to save the last 15–45 minutes for the Caring time.

[14] Early the next morning Abraham took some food and a skin of water and gave them to Hagar. He set them on her shoulders and then sent her off with the boy. She went on her way and wandered in the desert of Beersheba.

[15] When the water in the skin was gone, she put the boy under one of the bushes. [16] Then she went off and sat down nearby, about a bowshot away, for she thought, "I cannot watch the boy die." And as she sat there nearby, she began to sob.

[17] God heard the boy crying, and the angel of God called to Hagar from heaven and said to her, "What is the matter, Hagar? Do not be afraid; God has heard the boy crying as he lies there. [18] Lift the boy up and take him by the hand, for I will make him into a great nation."

[19] Then God opened her eyes and she saw a well of water. So she went and filled the skin with water and gave the boy a drink.

[20] God was with the boy as he grew up. He lived in the desert and became an archer.

Genesis 21:14–20

1. What amazes you most in this story?
   - ❐ that Abraham would send Hagar off with so little provisions in the first place
   - ❐ that God could hear one little child crying
   - ❐ that there was a well of water nearby that Hagar hadn't previously seen
   - ❐ that some stories do have happy endings

2. Hagar ran out of water for her child. What vital resource do you feel closest to running out of right now?
   ❐ money   ❐ energy
   ❐ patience   ❐ hope
   ❐ time   ❐ understanding
   ❐ other _____

3. When have you experienced something so devastating in your life that you could identify with Hagar?

4. God opened Hagar's eyes to a resource (the well) which she had not previously noticed. When, after going to God in prayer, has he opened your eyes to a resource you had not noticed before?

5. Comparing yourself to Hagar, what are your feelings about God?
   ❐ I feel bitter toward God because people like Abraham and Sarah have really let me down.
   ❐ I feel like God has forgotten about me and I'm out in the desert on my own.
   ❐ I'm hurting right now, but I do believe God hears me.
   ❐ God gives me what I need when I need it. I'm learning to trust.
   ❐ God has provided for me, but I'm still concerned about the future.

6. As you think now of the resources available to you, which are you under-using?
   ❐ the support of my friends
   ❐ the support of this group
   ❐ the support of my spouse or family
   ❐ books on spiritual discipline and guidance
   ❐ the spiritual insights of my pastor
   ❐ the insights of Scripture
   ❐ counseling agencies in our community
   ❐ other _____

7. Hagar listened to God in her aloneness and God gave her a promise for the future of her son. How do you react to the idea of using more of your prayer time to *listen* rather than talk?
   ❐ I would need a different kind of hearing aid to do that!
   ❐ I try—but all I get is static!
   ❐ How do I know when God is speaking—and when it's just me?
   ❐ I'm open to try.
   ❐ I'm doing that now, and here is how it has been working ...

CARING / 15–45 Minutes / All Together

Leader: Regather the entire group for the Caring time. The purpose of the Caring time in this session is to spend time in caring support for each other through sharing prayer requests and prayer.

SHARING

Take time to share any personal prayer requests. Think especially of resources you are in need of. Let the following responsive reading from Psalm 136 encourage you concerning God's loving resources. Have the leader read the first verse, then everyone say the refrain, *"His love endures forever,"* together in unison. Then have the person to the leader's left read the second verse, everyone say the refrain in unison, etc.

> *Give thanks to the Lord, for he is good.*
> > *His love endures forever.*
> *Give thanks to the God of gods.*
> > *His love endures forever.*
> *Give thanks to the Lord of lords:*
> > *His love endures forever.*
> *to him who alone does great wonders,*
> > *His love endures forever.*
> *who by his understanding made the heavens,*
> > *His love endures forever.*
> *who spread out the earth upon the waters,*
> > *His love endures forever.*
> *who made the great lights—*
> > *His love endures forever.*
> *the sun to govern the day,*
> > *His love endures forever.*
> *the moon and stars to govern the night;*
> > *His love endures forever.*
>
> . . .
>
> *to the One who remembered us in our low estate*
> > *His love endures forever.*
> *and freed us from our enemies,*
> > *His love endures forever.*
> *and who gives food to every creature.*
> > *His love endures forever.*
> *Give thanks to the God of heaven.*
> > *His love endures forever.*
> > *Psalm 136:1–9, 23–26*

PRAYER

Close with a time of prayer, remembering the requests that have been shared. If you would like to pray in silence, say the word "Amen" when you have finished your prayer, so the next person will know when to start.

<table>
<tr><td>SESSION
6</td><td colspan="2">## A Dry Past and Future</td></tr>
<tr><td></td><td>**LIFE STORIES**</td><td>**BIBLE STUDY**</td></tr>
</table>

PURPOSE

To introduce the subject of "A Dry Past and Future" and to support one another.

AGENDA

 Gathering   Study   Caring

OPEN

 GATHERING / 15 Minutes / All Together

Leader: Welcome the newcomers and explain the purpose and procedures of the group. Explain that this session is the first of two sessions on "A Dry Past and Future."

Start off by reading the Introduction to the group or ask for a volunteer to read it. Then, use the Ice-Breaker to start the meeting. Remember to keep to the 3-part agenda.

INTRODUCTION

Jesus taught "Each day has enough trouble of its own" (Matthew 6:34). Part of our problem is that it is difficult to follow that teaching. Today's spiritual dryness is often not the result of today's problems, but rather it is the result of unresolved guilt from the past, or anxiety about an uncertain future. To live out the spirit of Jesus' teaching takes discipline—spiritual discipline. We must deal with our past through the discipline of confession. Traditionally Protestants have sought to confess their sins to God alone, but there is value in confessing to a trusted human being—a friend or clergyperson. Not only can such a practice force us to let go of the pretense we sometimes have, but hearing God's forgiveness from another human being can make it more real to us. When another human being knows of our shortcomings, they can also encourage us to be more responsible in the future.

While confession helps us deal with our past, the discipline of submission helps us keep anxiety about the future from making for a spiritually dry present. Anxiety about the future comes when we expect to have more control of the future than we realistically can have. But submission to God and God's control of the future helps turn the future into an adventure. Maya Angelou says it well:

"Because of the routines we follow, we often forget that life is an ongoing adventure. We leave our homes for work, acting and even believing that we will reach our destinations with no unusual event startling

us out of our set expectations. The truth is that we know nothing, not where our cars will fail or when our buses will stall, whether our places of employment will be there when we arrive, or whether, in fact, we ourselves will arrive whole and alive at the end of our journeys. Life is a pure adventure, and the sooner we realize that, the quicker we will be able to treat life as art ..."¹

We will have two sessions on using confession and submission to deal with the dryness of past and future, and this is the first. In this session, the emphasis will be on sharing your own story. If you wish to spend another session on this topic and go deeper into this issue, you can choose to move to Track 2 for the next session ... or you can stay in Track 1 and move on to the next issue. This session has the same three-part agenda as the previous sessions. Use the following Ice-Breaker to get started.

Ice-Breaker: Life's Embarrassing Moments. As you look back over your past, which of the following transitions brought you the most embarrassment? Tell as much as you can remember about your experience so we can blush right along with you!

- ❐ going to a junior high dance and getting up nerve to ask someone to dance
- ❐ the first time I kissed someone of the opposite sex (outside of family)
- ❐ meeting my future in-laws for the first time and saying the wrong thing
- ❐ fixing that meal when we were first married and I tried a "new recipe"!
- ❐ that time at my first job when I realized they don't teach you everything in school
- ❐ the day I realized my teenager didn't want me around in public
- ❐ meeting my teenage child's date and saying the wrong thing

 STUDY / 30 Minutes / Groups of 4

Leader: If there are more than 7 in your group, quickly subdivide into groups of 4 so that everyone can participate, and you can finish the Study in 30 minutes. Then, call all of the groups back together for the Caring time.

Life Stories. Have someone read aloud the stories of the two people below. Then, use the questions to share some of your own experience.

Ben
By most standards Ben was a successful man. He had risen through his company to become one of its vice-presidents. He was a trustee in his church, and taught a Senior High Sunday School class. But then suddenly Ben just seemed to turn off spiritually. He couldn't explain why.

He resigned his office and his teaching position because he was feeling like a hypocrite, trying to teach something that was not exciting him. Finally his pastor convinced him to come in and talk about it. After a couple of sessions together, Ben started talking about an old love relationship. He confessed to his pastor that he had gotten this girl pregnant. No one except the girl knew he was the father, and Ben had never told the woman who was now his wife. As he talked about this situation tears came to his eyes. Ben figured the boy he fathered would be about 16 right now, the age he was when he got the girl pregnant, and the age of several boys in his Sunday School class. His pastor asked him if he had ever done anything to share in the responsibility of the child or to make amends in any way. He had not. As he admitted that, Ben realized how much guilt he had been carrying around all of this time. He decided to contact the mother to see if even at that late time he could be of help in providing for the boy's needs. While this confession put Ben under stress at first, he found in time that his relationship with God and his image of himself became stronger than ever.

Katrina

Katrina was one who never felt she could save enough money. Her husband, Ron, would try to get her to splurge every now and then, but she didn't feel she could do it. For a while it was beginning to pay off as they built a nice little savings. But then she had to have some surgery and her husband was laid off. Their savings quickly dwindled to nothing. For a long time Katrina was angry and frightened. She was angry because her life savings that she had worked so hard to build up was gone, and she was frightened because her husband was still out of work and they were financially vulnerable. Part of her anger was at her husband, even though she knew he was a hard worker and had not deserved to be laid off. Part of her anger was at God for letting it all happen. Part of her anger was even at herself, because she felt she should have saved even more. Finally, in desperation she went to her church sanctuary during the week when no one was there, and she just poured out her anger and her fear. After some time she looked up and saw the cross of Christ, and she remembered his suffering and the words he said before his death, "Father, into thy hands I commit my spirit." That phrase came to her mind again and again. She saw in it a statement of submission and trust. She realized that was the spirit she needed in her own situation. Whatever happened, she would commit herself into the hands of God. She left feeling more at peace than she had in a long time.

DISCUSS | **Questions:**

1. When you were in grade school or junior high, was there a time when you felt you had to "fess up" to something you had done wrong? Was it difficult or easy for you? How did you do?

2.   What do you find in either of these stories that is like your own story?
   ❏ Like Ben, most people would view me as successful.
   ❏ Like Ben, I have resigned from, or felt like resigning from, my church commitments because of "spiritual dryness."
   ❏ Like Ben, I made some mistakes in my past that still weigh me down.
   ❏ Like Katrina, I am a "saver."
   ❏ Like Katrina, my life collapsed when my savings collapsed.
   ❏ Like Katrina, I get angry when my future seems out of my control.

3.   Of the two disciplines we are talking about in this session, confession and submission, which do you find is hardest for you? What makes it so hard?

4.   The Introduction advises that confession to another trusted human being can help us, partly by forcing us to let go of the pretense we sometimes have, but also by helping us to receive God's forgiveness through that friend. How do you react to this idea?
   ❏ This is a new idea.
   ❏ This is a scary idea.
   ❏ I tried this once and the person I confessed to didn't know how to receive it.
   ❏ I have found the practice of confession very valuable.
   ❏ other _____

5.   How do you react to Maya Angelou's idea that once we accept how little of our future we really control, we can see life as "pure adventure"?
   ❏ I'm not the adventure type.
   ❏ Maybe if it were a somewhat safer adventure—like shooting the rapids!
   ❏ My future looks more predictable than an adventure.
   ❏ Adventures excite me—but they frighten me too!
   ❏ The future is an adventure—and God is my trail guide!

6.   In what area of your life do you find it hardest to submit yourself and your future in trust to God?
   ❏ in the area of financial security
   ❏ in facing death
   ❏ in regard to my professional future
   ❏ in regard to my family's well-being
   ❏ other _____

7. What would best help you to more fully submit to God's control of your future?
   ☐ having support and encouragement from other Christian friends
   ☐ more use of meditation and prayer
   ☐ more inspirational stories of people who found peace through submission
   ☐ I don't know if I am ready for that yet.
   ☐ other _____

 CARING / 15–45 Minutes / All Together

Leader: To close this session, call the groups back together to join in the sharing and prayer.

SHARING

Reciting Scriptures that speak of submitting to God in trust is one way we remind ourselves to follow that discipline. Recite together as a group the following Psalm, which is one of the most-loved of all Scriptures and which speaks of how we can entrust ourselves to God. Pause after each sentence to meditate.

> *"The Lord is my shepherd, I shall not be in want. /*
> *   He makes me lie down in green pastures,*
> *he leads me beside quiet waters,*
> *   he restores my soul. /*
> *He guides me in the path of righteousness*
> *   for his name's sake. /*
> *Even though I walk*
> *   through the valley of the shadow of death*
> *I will fear no evil,*
> *   for you are with me;*
> *your rod and your staff,*
> *   they comfort me. /*
> *You prepare a table before me*
> *   in the presence of my enemies. /*
> *You anoint my head with oil;*
> *   my cup overflows. /*
> *Surely goodness and love will follow me*
> *   all the days of my life,*
> *and I will dwell in the house of the Lord forever."*
>
> *Psalm 23*

PRAYER

Some translations of "the valley of the shadow of death" say "the valley of dark shadows." What "dark shadow" do you feel lies across your future? Share with the group.

Remembering what people shared, close in prayer, asking God to help us trust him in the midst of our "dark shadows." Again, remember that if you would like to pray in silence, say the word "Amen" when you have finished your prayer, so the next person will know when to start.

<table>
<tr><td>SESSION</td><td rowspan="2">

A Dry Past and Future
</td></tr>
<tr><td>

7
</td></tr>
</table>

LIFE STORIES	BIBLE STUDY

PURPOSE To go deeper into the issue of "A Dry Past and Future" and to identify with a story in Scripture related to this topic.

AGENDA   Gathering   Study   Caring

OPEN   **GATHERING** / 15 Minutes / All Together
Leader: Welcome newcomers and explain the purpose and the procedures of the group. Explain that this session is the second of two sessions on "A Dry Past and Future."
The purpose of the Gathering time is to break the ice. Call time after 15 minutes and move on.

Ice-Breaker: Past, Present and Future. If time is limited you may want to share in just two of the following areas.

PAST: If I were young again, I would spend more time:
- ❐ reading great books
- ❐ talking about ...
- ❐ working on community projects
- ❐ getting involved in church
- ❐ loving my friends
- ❐ praying
- ❐ playing
- ❐ with my family
- ❐ stopping to smell the flowers
- ❐ other _____

PRESENT: Life would be better if there were more:
- ❐ parades
- ❐ county fairs
- ❐ mom and pop stores
- ❐ clean mountain streams
- ❐ free concerts
- ❐ family picnics
- ❐ homemade bread
- ❐ square dances
- ❐ espresso stands
- ❐ other _____

FUTURE: No matter how old I get, I hope I am still able to:
- ❐ make love
- ❐ grow flowers
- ❐ play with children
- ❐ make people laugh
- ❐ take a joke
- ❐ earn a living
- ❐ drive a car
- ❐ take care of myself
- ❐ walk a mile
- ❐ play a sport
- ❐ listen to rock music
- ❐ other _____

STUDY / 30 Minutes / Groups of 4

Leader: If you have more than 7 in your group, we recommend subdividing into groups of 4 (4 at the dining table, 4 at the kitchen table, etc.) so that you can finish the Study in 30 minutes and everyone can participate.

INTRODUCTION

Old Dry Bones. Ezekiel prophesied when Israel was in exile in Babylonia. It was perhaps the lowest point of their history. They were separated from their homeland, and their hope of being revived as a nation was fading. During this time, Ezekiel went to an old battlefield, perhaps one where Israel had lost a battle which led to their captivity and exile. The field was full of old, dry human bones from the battle, and Ezekiel saw these as symbolic of the spirit of Israel. His vision of the bones coming to life was symbolic of Israel finding a new life and identity.

Ever since this prophecy, people who are down and out have seen it as a message that with God there is always hope. This hope was especially meaningful to the slaves of America's Old South who turned the story into the spiritual song, "Dem Bones." It spoke to them of their crushed hope being revived through a new life of freedom. As you read, find the images of your own spiritual dryness.

Have someone in your group read the passage out loud. Then go around on the first question and let everyone speak up. Then go around again on the next question, etc. Be sure to save the last 15–45 minutes for the Caring time.

37 *The hand of the Lord was upon me, and he brought me out by the Spirit of the LORD and set me in the middle of a valley; it was full of bones. ²He led me back and forth among them, and I saw a great many bones on the floor of the valley, bones that were very dry. ³He asked me, "Son of man, can these bones live?"*

I said, "O Sovereign LORD, you alone know."

⁴Then he said to me, "Prophesy to these bones and say to them, 'Dry bones, hear the word of the LORD! ⁵This is what the Sovereign LORD says to these bones: I will make breath enter you, and you will come to life. ⁶I will attach tendons to you and make flesh come upon you and cover you with skin; I will put breath in you, and you will come to life. Then you will know that I am the LORD.' "

⁷So I prophesied as I was commanded. And as I was prophesying, there was a noise, a rattling sound, and the bones came together, bone to bone. ⁸I looked, and tendons and flesh appeared on them and skin covered them, but there was no breath in them.

⁹Then he said to me, "Prophesy to the breath; prophesy, son of man, and say to it, 'This is what the Sovereign LORD says: Come from the four winds, O breath, and breathe into these slain, that they may live.' " ¹⁰So I prophesied as he commanded me, and breath entered them; they came to life and stood on their feet—a vast army.

¹¹Then he said to me: "Son of man, these bones are the whole house of Israel." They say, "Our bones are dried up and our hope is gone; we are cut off.' [12]Therefore prophesy and say to them: 'This is what the Sovereign LORD says: O my people, I am going to open your graves and bring you up from them; I will bring you back to the land of Israel. [13]Then you, my people, will know that I am the LORD, when I open your graves and bring you up from them. [14]I will put my Spirit in you and you will live, and I will settle you in your own land. Then you will know that I the LORD have spoken, and I have done it, declares the LORD.' "*

Ezekiel 37:1–14

1. How would you have felt if God had led you to a valley of old, dry human bones?
   - ❑ spooked
   - ❑ bewildered
   - ❑ meditative
   - ❑ peaceful
   - ❑ depressed at the thought of death
   - ❑ intellectually stimulated (I could play archaeologist!)
   - ❑ cynical about war and human nature

2. If God asked you the question, "Can these bones live?" how would you have responded?
   - ❑ I would have laughed!
   - ❑ "Wow! Poltergeist, Part III!"
   - ❑ "I hope not! I'm afraid of ghosts!"
   - ❑ I would have figured it was a trick question.
   - ❑ I would have thought he was referring to the afterlife.
   - ❑ I would have responded like Ezekiel: "Lord, you alone know."

3. What in you has died in the battles of your life, and now seems like old dry bones?
   - ❑ my belief that good people are rewarded
   - ❑ my belief that I can ever find peace
   - ❑ my belief that problems can be resolved
   - ❑ my belief that I will ever really understand myself
   - ❑ my belief that I will ever be happy
   - ❑ my belief in women
   - ❑ my belief in men
   - ❑ none of the above—All of my hopes are alive and well!

4. Where are you in the process of bringing your spiritual life back to life again?
   - ❑ seeing only the old, dry bones that are left of what used to be
   - ❑ A few things are clicking and rattling, but nothing has come together yet.
   - ❑ The "skeleton" is together, but there is no "meat" on it yet.
   - ❑ Everything is together, but there is no "breath"—I see a vision, but have not brought it to life.
   - ❑ It's ALIVE!—and I'm back on my feet!

CARING / 15–45 Minutes / All Together

Leader: Spend some time evaluating the experience in the group up to this point. Then, close with prayer.

EVALUATION

This is the midpoint in this course. Use this opportunity to take your pulse and make any necessary mid-course corrections. Start off with the exercises below. Then, close in prayer.

How would you describe your small group? Choose one of the images below which best describes your small group, then go around your group and tell them why you chose the one you did.

AN ORCHARD: Whenever I'm in this group I feel like a fragrant, healthy apple tree because of all the growing I've done and all the fruit I've been able to share.

BIRD NEST: I know how a baby bird feels because being a part of this group makes me feel nurtured and protected.

OASIS: While the rest of the world can be so harsh and unforgiving, this group is a refreshing stop on the journey of life.

THE 12 MUSKETEERS: It's "All for one and one for all" with this group. I always feel like I belong and I'm part of a great team.

A LITTER OF PUPPIES: You are a fun, friendly and enthusiastic bundle of joy. I feel younger every time we are together.

M*A*S*H* UNIT: This group is like a field hospital. I came in wounded and now I feel so much better and I have a bunch of friends to boot!

TEEPEE: We couldn't stand tall and provide warmth and shelter if we didn't lean on each other.

THE BRADY BUNCH: I feel like I'm part of one big happy family. We're not perfect, but we love and accept each other.

THINK TANK: This group must be full of geniuses! We seem to be able to understand every issue and work out every problem with creativity and discernment.

PRAYER

Close with a time of prayer. If you would like to pray in silence, say the word "Amen," when you have finished your prayer, so that the next person will know when to start.

<table>
<tr><td rowspan="2">SESSION
8</td><td colspan="2"><h1>Feeling Lonely</h1></td></tr>
<tr><td>LIFE STORIES</td><td>BIBLE STUDY</td></tr>
</table>

PURPOSE   To introduce the issue of "Feeling Lonely" and continue to support each other.

AGENDA   Gathering   Study   Caring

OPEN

 GATHERING / 15 Minutes / All Together

Leader: Welcome newcomers and explain the purpose and procedures in this group. Explain that this session is the first session on "Feeling Lonely."

Start off by reading the Introduction to the group or ask for a volunteer to read it. Then, use the Ice-Breaker to start the meeting. Remember to keep to the 3-part agenda.

INTRODUCTION

Deserts are often lonely places. That's true whether we are talking of a literal desert or a spiritual one. Sometimes it's difficult to tell during times of spiritual dryness who we feel most isolated from—God or other people. But the two go together—we experience God in the context of the fellowship we are in.

When spiritual dryness includes a sense of being isolated and lonely, then the two spiritual disciplines which become particularly important are worship and celebration. Worship is not just to put us in touch with God—it's also to put us in touch with God's family. That's why listening to a TV preacher is inadequate. The TV preacher can preach the best sermon in the world, but if we are alone in our home, feeling isolated from the rest of God's family, we have not fully worshiped. Even worshipping in a church can be inadequate if it does not put us in touch with both God and others. As Richard Foster writes, "We can use all the right techniques and methods, we can have the best possible liturgy, but we have not worshiped the Lord until Spirit touches spirit."[1]

Closely related to the discipline of worship is celebration. Celebration is joining together with others in the family of God to enjoy life and praise God for the gift of that life. Such a sense of celebration can change our attitude toward life. Dallas Willard writes, "Celebration heartily done makes our deprivations and sorrows seem small, and we find in it great strength to do the will of our God because his goodness becomes so real to us."[2]

We will have two sessions on the role of worship and celebration in counteracting our loneliness, and this is the first. In this session, the emphasis will be on sharing your own story. If you wish to spend another session on this topic and go deeper into this issue, you can choose to move to Track 2 for the next session ... or you can stay in Track 1 and go on to the next issue.

This is the first of two sessions on "Feeling Lonely." Use the Ice-Breaker to get started.

Ice-Breaker: Desert Island. If you were stranded on a desert island, which of the following persons would you like to be stranded with, and why?

❐ Jacques Cousteau   ❐ Jimmy Carter
❐ Tom Cruise   ❐ Gilligan
❐ Mother Teresa   ❐ Robin Williams
❐ Pope John Paul II   ❐ Julia Roberts
❐ Colin Powell   ❐ Bill Gates
❐ Bob Vila   ❐ Sandi Patti
❐ Robert Schuller   ❐ Dr. C. Everett Koop

STUDY / 30 Minutes / Groups of 4

Leader: If there are more than 7 in your group, quickly sub-divide into groups of 4 so that everyone can participate, and you can finish the Study in 30 minutes. Then, call all of the groups back together for the Caring time.

Life Stories. Have someone read aloud the stories of the two people below. Then, use the questions to share some of your own experience.

Paul
Paul was raised in a small town where conservative values predominated. As Paul reached high school age, he more and more saw the people of his town as hypocritical. They didn't allow dancing, but some of the people who led the fight against dancing establishments were known to be having affairs. They spoke of their concern for their neighbors, but people often gossiped behind the backs of their neighbors. Strangers, especially strangers of another race, were ostracized from their social circles. For these reasons when Paul got married and moved away, he stayed away from churches. He saw them as places full of the hypocrisy he had seen as a child and youth. He still believed in God, but he felt he could worship him better on his own. As time went on, however, Paul began to feel more and more spiritually empty. He had no one who he could relate to on spiritual matters. He knew people at work who spoke of groups they were a member of where they could share honestly about

their feelings and their relationship with God. Others spoke of uplifting experiences they had at worship. Paul longed for such experiences, but still his childhood memories made him hold back.

Marie

Marie has attended her present church for the past two years. But she doesn't feel quite satisfied. She feels the preaching is good, but she feels isolated. She sees most of the people who worship there as being unexcited about what they are doing. They seem to be just going through the motions. In addition, nobody talks to anyone outside of their small circles of friends. Instead of feeling uplifted when she leaves, she feels let down. She wonders what she should do—go to another church, try to change this one, or simply learn to accept things the way they are.

DISCUSS

Questions:

1. When I was a child I thought of church as something ...
   - ❏ like a museum or library—where you talk in hushed tones and don't touch.
   - ❏ like an extended family—to eat potlucks with.
   - ❏ like the dentist's office—a place my parents made me go.
   - ❏ like school—only where you learn about God.
   - ❏ like a theater—where the people up front entertain you.
   - ❏ like a rest home—full of old people.
   - ❏ like a playground—full of good places to play and hide.

2. How would you compare your experience of worship with that of Paul and Marie? (Mark as many as apply.)
   - ❏ Like Paul I have tended to avoid worshipping in church as an adult.
   - ❏ Like Paul I see most church people as hypocritical.
   - ❏ Like Paul I don't feel I have anyone I can really relate to on spiritual matters.
   - ❏ Like Paul, bad past experiences hinder me from reaching out to become part of a church family I could worship with.
   - ❏ Like Marie I see most people in church as bored or unexcited.
   - ❏ Like Marie I feel isolated even while in church worship.
   - ❏ Like Marie I have considered leaving my present church.

3. Both Paul and Marie in the stories above felt isolated. To what degree is a sense of isolation part of your "spiritual dryness"? Mark the following scale:

1	2	3	4	5	6	7	8	9	10
not at all		a minor factor			a major factor				the central factor

4. Richard Foster is quoted in the Introduction as writing of worship, "We can use all the right techniques and methods, we can have the best possible liturgy, but we have not worshiped the Lord until Spirit touches spirit." From your experience, which of the following has most frequently made it possible for "Spirit to touch spirit" in your life?
    - ❏ singing from the heart
    - ❏ honest sharing by a fellow struggler
    - ❏ eloquent preaching
    - ❏ people working together to help someone out
    - ❏ a properly timed hug
    - ❏ symbolic acts, like communion
    - ❏ expressive religious art
    - ❏ other _____

5. Dallas Willard is quoted in the Introduction as writing, "Celebration heartily done makes our deprivations and sorrows seem small, and we find in it great strength to do the will of our God because his goodness becomes so real to us." Do you agree? Why or why not?

6. What do you need to do to make celebration a regular part of your spiritual life?
    - ❏ attend worship more often
    - ❏ take time to "count my blessings"
    - ❏ praise God every night for the blessings of that day
    - ❏ learn some celebrative songs
    - ❏ play celebrative Christian music
    - ❏ other _____

CARING / 15–45 Minutes / All Together

Leader: Regather everyone for the Caring time. Spend some time sharing, then close in prayer.

SHARING

Have someone in the group share one thing they have to celebrate at this point in their life. Then, as a group, sing the doxology below. Then, ask another person to share and sing the Doxology together again etc. around the group.

> *"Praise God from whom all blessings flow,*
> *Praise him all creatures here below*
> *Praise him above ye heavenly host*
> *Praise Father, Son and Holy Ghost!"*

PRAYER

Close with a time of prayer, thanking God for your blessings, and asking God for a greater spirit of celebration. If you would like to pray in silence, say the word "Amen" when you have finished your prayer, so that the next person will know when to start.

NOTES:

[1]Richard J. Foster, *Celebration of Discipline* (San Francisco: Harper & Row, 1978), p. 138.
[2]Dallas Willard, *The Spirit of the Disciplines* (San Francisco: Harper & Row, 1988), p. 181.

Feeling Lonely

LIFE STORIES	BIBLE STUDY

PURPOSE

To go deeper into the subject of "Feeling Lonely" by relating your experience to a story in Scripture.

AGENDA

 Gathering   **Study**   **Caring**

OPEN

GATHERING / 15 Minutes / All Together

Leader: Welcome newcomers and explain the purpose and procedure of the group. Explain that this session is the second of two sessions on the issue of "Feeling Lonely."

The purpose of the Gathering time is to break the ice. Call time after 15 minutes and move on.

Ice-Breaker: Like Music to My Ears. Which of each of the following pairs of sounds is most likely to be "like music to your ears." Give each person a chance to finish the sentence by answering four or five of the pairs below: "It's like music to my ears to hear ... "

the crackling of a campfire . . . . the sounds of city traffic at night

the cry of "play ball!" . . . . waves crashing against the shore

the laughter of children . . . . the laughter of an adult party

a train whistle in the distance . . . . the bell of an ice cream truck

the ring of the telephone . . . . the ring of a cash register

the gurgling of . . . . the talk of an
a mountain stream   opening-night crowd

the purr of a kitten . . . . the hum of a well-tuned engine

the silence of new-fallen snow . . . . the cheering of a crowd

the sound of gentle rain. . . . . the rapid talk of an auctioneer

the chirping of a bird . . . . the crackling of a thunderstorm

Leader: If you have more than 7 in your group, we recommend subdividing into groups of 4 (4 at the dining table, 4 at the kitchen table, etc.) so that you can finish the Study in 30 minutes and everyone can participate.

INTRODUCTION

A **"Lone Ranger."** Elijah lived under the reign of perhaps the most wicked king and queen of Israel's history—Ahab and Jezebel. Ahab and Jezebel sought to get the people to follow foreign gods (called Baals), and in the following passage they seek to kill Elijah, God's greatest prophet of that time. So bad was the moral climate of the time that Elijah came to feel like he was battling totally alone. In his despair he flees to the desert, but there learns that he is not as alone as he thought.

Have someone read the passage out loud. Then, go around on the first question and let everyone speak up. Then, go around on the next question, etc. Be sure to save the last 15–45 minutes for the Caring time.

19 *Now Ahab told Jezebel everything Elijah had done and how he had killed all the prophets with the sword. ²So Jezebel sent a messenger to Elijah to say, "May the gods deal with me, be it ever so severely, if by this time tomorrow I do not make your life like that of one of them."*

³Elijah was afraid and ran for his life. When he came to Beersheba in Judah, he left his servant there, ⁴while he himself went a day's journey into the desert. He came to a broom tree, sat down under it and prayed that he might die. "I have had enough, Lord," he said, "Take my life; I am no better than my ancestors." ⁵Then he lay down under the tree and fell asleep.

All at once an angel touched him and said, "Get up and eat." ⁶He looked around, and there by his head was a cake of bread baked over hot coals, and a jar of water. He ate and drank and then lay down again.

⁷The angel of the Lord came back a second time and touched him and said, "Get up and eat, for the journey is too much for you." ⁸So he got up and ate and drank. Strengthened by that food, he traveled forty days and forty nights until he reached Horeb, the mountain of God. ⁹There he went into a cave and spent the night.

And the word of the Lord came to him: "What are you doing here, Elijah?"

¹⁰He replied, "I have been very zealous for the Lord God Almighty. The Israelites have rejected your covenant, broken down your altars, and put your prophets to death with the sword. I am the only one left, and now they are trying to kill me too."

¹¹The Lord said, "Go out and stand on the mountain in the presence of the Lord, for the Lord is about to pass by."

Then a great and powerful wind tore the mountains apart and shattered the rocks before the Lord, but the Lord was not in the wind. After the wind there was an earthquake, but the Lord was not in the earthquake. ¹²After the earthquake came a fire, but the Lord was not in the fire. And after the fire came a gentle whisper. ¹³When Elijah heard it, he pulled his cloak over his face and went out and stood at the mouth of the cave.

Then a voice said to him, "What are you doing here, Elijah?"

¹⁴He replied, "I have been very zealous for the Lord God Almighty. The Israelites have rejected your covenant, broken down your altars, and put your prophets to death with the sword. I am the only one left, and now they are trying to kill me too."

¹⁵The Lord said to him, "Go back the way you came, and go to the Desert of Damascus. When you get there, anoint Hazael king over Aram. ¹⁶Also, anoint Jehu son of Nimshi king over Israel, and anoint Elisha son of Shaphat from Abel Meholah to succeed you as prophet. ¹⁷Jehu will put to death any who escape the sword of Hazael, and Elisha will put to death any who escape the sword of Jehu. ¹⁸Yet I reserve seven thousand in Israel—all whose knees have not bowed down to Baal and all whose mouths have not kissed him."

1 Kings 19:1–18

"The epistles speak frequently of the believing community as 'the body of Christ.' As human life is unthinkable without head, arms, and legs, so it was unthinkable for those [early] Christians to live in isolation from one another."
—Richard J. Foster in *Celebration of Discipline*

1. How would you describe Elijah, based on this story?
   - ❏ violent
   - ❏ prudent
   - ❏ zealous
   - ❏ disciplined
   - ❏ self-pitying
   - ❏ mystical
   - ❏ faithful
   - ❏ cowardly

2. Why do you think Elijah wanted to end his life?
   - ❏ He felt like a failure as a prophet.
   - ❏ It would be better than living in fear.
   - ❏ He felt intense loneliness.
   - ❏ He didn't really—he was just feeling sorry for himself.

3. What did Elijah need the most?
   - ❏ physical replenishment
   - ❏ a quiet and peaceful spiritual retreat
   - ❏ an attitude adjustment
   - ❏ some answers about life
   - ❏ fellowship with other believers
   - ❏ a fresh vision of God

4. Elijah looked for God in a variety of natural phenomena—wind, earthquakes and fire. When have you been around a natural phenomenon, like a hurricane, tornado, earthquake, etc., that particularly spoke to you of God's power?

5. What does it say to you that in the end God spoke to Elijah through a whisper, rather than through a violent act of nature?
   - ❏ God is subtle.
   - ❏ God is gentle.
   - ❏ You have to slow down and be quiet before you hear God.
   - ❏ If we are looking for God we should look to the voice within us.
   - ❏ other _____

6. Why do you think Elijah felt like he was the only God-fearing person left if there were in reality 7000 others like him?
   - ❏ He was too busy playing the "Lone Ranger."
   - ❏ He liked feeling sorry for himself.
   - ❏ He just assumed everyone else was a hypocrite.
   - ❏ Maybe they were afraid to come out and worship God in the open.
   - ❏ other _____

7. What do you need to do to find other spiritually searching people like you, who can help you overcome your spiritual dryness?
   - ❏ stick with this group!
   - ❏ stop trying to be a spiritual "Lone Ranger"
   - ❏ have the courage to admit my faith and doubts, so I can connect with others like me
   - ❏ other_____

CARING / 15–45 Minutes / All Together

Leader: You have two options for this Caring time. One would be to bring the whole group back together for a time of prayer requests and prayer, as you have done in previous sessions. The other would be to follow Option 2 to share some appreciation for others in your group.

OPTION 1

Take time to share any prayer requests by answering the question below. Then close with a time of prayer, remembering the requests that have been shared and the needs for connecting with others and hearing God's voice. If you would like to pray in silence, say the word "Amen" when you have finished your prayer, so that the next person will know when to start.

"How can we help you in prayer this week?"

OPTION 2

You have probably been richly blessed by the people in your small group. Now is the time to tell them how they have blessed you.

Ask one person to sit in silence while the others go around and finish one of the sentences below about this person. Then, ask another person to remain silent while you go around again, etc.

- ❏ You have blessed me recently when you told the story about ...
- ❏ What inspires me most about your character is ...
- ❏ The aspect of your personality I would like to adopt into my own is ...
- ❏ You have a way with people that I admire very much ...
- ❏ There is something about your faith in God that I really like ...

Waiting for God

| LIFE STORIES | BIBLE STUDY |

PURPOSE

To introduce the subject of "Waiting for God" and share your own stories.

AGENDA

 Gathering Study Caring

OPEN

 GATHERING / 15 Minutes / All Together

Leader: Welcome newcomers and explain the purpose and procedures in this course. Explain that this is the first of two sessions on the issue of "Waiting for God."

Start off by reading the Introduction to the group or ask for a volunteer to read it. Then, use the Ice-Breaker to start the meeting. Remember to keep to the 3-part agenda.

INTRODUCTION

In today's world people are getting less and less patient with having to wait for what they want. We see a product we want, we "buy now, pay later." We don't have to wait for our tax refund—we get it right away from the company that figures our tax. Mail is too slow now—if we want to send a message, we fax it or send it E-mail. Fast food restaurants thrive because they require little waiting. Perhaps that is why we get particularly frustrated when we want God right now—and we have to wait! Perhaps God should develop a quick "drive-up window"!

Spiritual dryness often entails waiting for God. We feel distant from God. We feel spiritual need. We want to do something or take something that will take care of our problem right away. But instead we have to wait.

Part of the reason we have to wait is that the problem of spiritual dryness is often related to a lifestyle problem. When we have a lifestyle problem that is creating our need, God isn't going to just "fix it." He's going to try to help us see we have a lifestyle problem, and sometimes that takes time. Over time we have allowed other interests to take God's place in our life. Oh, we may still have gone to church, but more and more of our life's energy becomes focused on *things*. We let these things—success, expensive adult "toys," etc.—become our gods for us. They become what our life focuses on rather than God. That's why an important discipline to counteract this aspect of spiritual dryness is "simplicity." Simplicity is not asceticism, giving up all the pleasures of this world. Rather it's enjoying the simple goodness of life. We might possess some things, but we *never* let them possess *us*. Simplicity acknowledges the teaching of Jesus that "life is more important than food and the body more important than clothes" (Matthew 6:25). It's also turning away from the consumer-oriented approach to life where we see ourselves needing to be served—and quickly! It's learning that sometimes a life that is good and solid and worth living, requires some waiting.

We will have two sessions on the matter of "Waiting for God" in our spiritual dryness, and the role "simplicity" can take, and this is the first. In this session, the emphasis will be on sharing your own story. If you wish to spend another session on this topic and go deeper into this issue, you can choose to move to Track 2 for the next session ... or you can stay in Track 1 and go on to the next issue. Use the following Ice-Breaker to get started.

Ice-Breaker: Four Basic Food Groups. Go around on question 1 and let everyone share a page out of their life. Then go around again on question 2.

1. If you were to choose equivalents of the "four basic food groups" to nourish your emotional well-being ("religious" activities not included!) what would they be?

   ❒ getting hugs from friends
   ❒ attention from the opposite sex
   ❒ shopping
   ❒ watching old movies
   ❒ playing with my grandchildren
   ❒ camping in the mountains
   ❒ listening to music
   ❒ having time alone
   ❒ jogging
   ❒ other _____

   ❒ watching my "soaps"
   ❒ professional success
   ❒ watching sports on TV
   ❒ reading romance novels
   ❒ traveling
   ❒ fishing
   ❒ laying on the beach
   ❒ talking on the phone
   ❒ taking a walk

2. Which of the above do you feel most "hungry" for right now?

 STUDY / 30 Minutes / Groups of 4

Leader: If there are more than 7 in your group, we recommend that you subdivide into groups of 4 so that everyone can participate and you can finish the Study in 30 minutes.

Life Stories. Have someone read out loud the stories of the two people below. Then, use the questions to share some of your own experience.

Connie
Connie is frustrated. It just doesn't seem to her that she and her husband are progressing in life as fast as she thinks they should be. It seems all

her friends are better off financially than they are. Her friends vacation in Puerto Vallarta or Hawaii—she and her husband, if they take a vacation, visit her family in a small town in the Midwest. Her friends seem to be able to eat out in a nice restaurant seemingly every week. Connie and her husband are lucky to eat out one or two times a year. In spite of this, the family is "maxing out" on their credit cards. Connie prays about this frequently, but nothing has changed.

Jerry
Jerry is by most people's standards a success in business. His business has increased profits every year, and he has a large variety of investments, most of which are also doing well. He regularly attends church, and is on the church's board of trustees. But if you ask Jerry, he will admit that he really is not happy. Outside of his wife, he doesn't have any real friends, and his spiritual life has been less than fulfilling. He is greatly stirred by the music at his church, and occasionally by the sermons, but when he prays he often feels like no one is there.

DISCUSS | **Questions:**

1. What part of the two stories above sounds like your own?
   - ❒ feeling frustrated over lack of financial progress, like Connie
   - ❒ feeling others have more than I/we do, like Connie
   - ❒ being "maxed out" on my credit, like Connie
   - ❒ praying, but not seeing any results, like Connie
   - ❒ feeling I don't have many real friends, like Jerry
   - ❒ feeling sometimes like no one is listening when I pray, like Jerry

2. How would you describe your family's financial condition, in comparison to the people in these two stories?
   - ❒ rather comfortable, like Jerry
   - ❒ doing pretty well, but not as good as Jerry
   - ❒ struggling, like Connie
   - ❒ My situation makes Connie look like Donald Trump!

3. The Introduction says that sometimes we have to wait when we ask God to help with our spiritual need, because we have a lifestyle problem that God can only help us change over time. Do you agree? Why or why not?

4. In the Introduction it also says, "We might possess some things, but we never let them possess us." What should a person do to make sure that what he or she possesses does not possess them?

5. What relationship do you see between your attitude toward possessions / financial security and the experience of spiritual dryness? (Mark the continuum below):

1	2	3	4	5
None!		Some, but only secondarily		It's a central issue!

6. How receptive would you be to simplifying your lifestyle?
    - ❑ No way! I love my "toys"!
    - ❑ Well, maybe if I knew I absolutely had to!
    - ❑ If I saw others doing it, I might consider it.
    - ❑ I want to, but I'm not sure I can.
    - ❑ I'm ready, willing and able!

7. In what ways should the fact that "we can't take it with us" influence the way we live?
    - ❑ We should be more giving to others in need.
    - ❑ We should hoard and accumulate until right before we die.
    - ❑ We should sit back and let God (and the government) take care of us.
    - ❑ We should continually seek God's contentment and guidance for how we spend money.

8. How content are you in each of the following areas of your life? Write the percent of your contentment on the lines below to indicate where you are—somewhere between 0% contentment (Panic Button) and 100% contentment (No Problem) for each category:

    _____ my family   _____ my job / career

    _____ my personal life   _____ my relationship with friends

    _____ my health   _____ my relationship with God

    _____ finances   _____ the future

9. In which of these areas above, or another, do you sense God might be prompting you to reconsider your goals or priorities and adopt a simpler approach, giving God control?

CARING / 15–45 Minutes / All Together

Leader: Regather all the groups of 4 back together. Use the following quotation for your sharing time and then move into a time of prayer.

SHARING

Thomas Merton has written much on the contemplative life, having spent many periods in solitude and meditation. Read together the following quote from his book *Thoughts in Solitude*. Spend a few minutes sharing your thoughts on what he says about how our lifestyle relates to our spiritual life.

> *"If you want to have a spiritual life you must unify your life. A life is either all spiritual or not spiritual at all. No man can serve two masters. Your life is shaped by the end you live for. You are made in the image of what you desire.*
>
> *To unify your life, unify your desires. To spiritualize your life, spiritualize your desires. To spiritualize your desires, desire to be without desire."* [1]

PRAYER

Now move into a time of prayer, sharing prayer requests and then praying for one another's needs. If you would like to pray in silence, say the word "Amen" when you have finished your prayer, so the next person will know when to start.

NOTE:

[1]Thomas Merton, *Thoughts in Solitude* (New York: Farrar, Straus and Giroux, 1958), p. 56.

Waiting for God

| LIFE STORIES | BIBLE STUDY |

PURPOSE

To go deeper into the subject of "Waiting for God" and to look at a story in Scripture.

AGENDA

 Gathering   Study   Caring

OPEN

 ## GATHERING / 15 Minutes / All Together

Leader: Welcome newcomers and explain the purpose and procedures of the group. Explain that this session is the second of two on the issue of "Waiting for God."

The purpose of the Gathering time is to break the ice. Call time after 15 minutes and move on.

Ice Breaker: I Can't Wait. In which of the following situations would you have the hardest time waiting if the event in question were two weeks away?

- ❐ You have tickets to the Super Bowl.
- ❐ Your favorite out-of-town relative is coming for a visit.
- ❐ A company is preparing to announce who gets the great job for which you are a candidate.
- ❐ Your child has the lead role in his or her first high school play or musical.
- ❐ You've ordered a new car from the factory.
- ❐ You're going to Hawaii for your vacation.
- ❐ You're 8 1/2 months pregnant (or your daughter is!).

 ## STUDY / 30 Minutes / Groups of 4

Leader: If you have more than 7 in your group, we recommend subdividing into groups of 4 (4 at the dining table, 4 at the kitchen table, etc.) so that you can finish the Study in 30 minutes and everyone can participate. Be sure to save the last 15–45 minutes for the Caring time.

"gods 'r Us." In the following story the people of Israel are waiting for word from God. Moses has already led them out of captivity, and now he is on Mt. Sinai receiving, among other laws and instructions, the Ten Commandments. But the people get impatient with waiting. They want a god who will be available to them right away. So they go to Moses' brother Aaron to have him make them some gods in the manner of the surrounding polytheistic nations. Are there parallels with people of today?

Have someone in your group read the story out loud. Then, go around on the first question and let anyone speak up. Then, go around on the next questions, etc. Be sure to save the last 15–45 minutes for the Caring time.

32 *When the people saw that Moses was so long in coming down from the mountain, they gathered around Aaron and said, "Come, make us gods who will go before us. As for this fellow Moses who brought us up out of Egypt, we don't know what has happened to him."*

²Aaron answered them, "Take off the gold earrings that your wives, your sons and your daughters are wearing, and bring them to me." ³So all the people took off their earrings and brought them to Aaron. ⁴He took what they handed him and made it into an idol cast in the shape of a calf, fashioning it with a tool. Then they said, "These are your gods, O Israel, who brought you up out of Egypt."

⁵When Aaron saw this, he built an altar in front of the calf and announced, "Tomorrow there will be a festival to the Lord." ⁶So the next day the people rose early and sacrificed burnt offerings and presented fellowship offerings. Afterward they sat down to eat and drink and got up to indulge in revelry.

⁷Then the Lord said to Moses, "Go down, because your people, whom you brought up out of Egypt, have become corrupt. ⁸They have been quick to turn away from what I commanded them and have made themselves an idol cast in the shape of a calf. They have bowed down to it and sacrificed to it and have said, 'These are your gods, O Israel, who brought you up out of Egypt.'

⁹"I have seen these people," the Lord said to Moses, "and they are a stiff-necked people. ¹⁰Now leave me alone so that my anger may burn against them and that I may destroy them. Then I will make you into a great nation."

¹¹But Moses sought the favor of the Lord his God. "O Lord," he said, "why should your anger burn against your people, whom you brought out of Egypt with great power and a mighty hand? ¹²Why should the Egyptians say, 'It was with evil intent that he brought them out, to kill them in the mountains and to wipe them off the face of the earth'? Turn from your fierce anger; relent and do not bring disaster on your people. ¹³Remember your servants Abraham, Isaac and Israel, to whom you swore by your own self: 'I will make your descendants as numerous as the stars in the sky and I will give your descendants all this land I promised them, and it will be their inheritance forever.' " ¹⁴Then the Lord relented and did not bring on his people the disaster he had threatened.

Exodus 32:1–14

1. What do you perceive to have been the mood of the people of Israel when they asked Aaron to make gods for them?
   - ❒ bored
   - ❒ in the mood for a party
   - ❒ insecure and seeking someone to direct them
   - ❒ rebellious
   - ❒ confused
   - ❒ other _____

2. Why were the people so quick to accept this golden calf as a god?
   - ❒ They were primitive and gullible.
   - ❒ At least it was a god you could see.
   - ❒ It was shiny and impressive looking.
   - ❒ They wanted a god they could control.
   - ❒ Aaron said it was a god, and he was their "expert."

3. What was the hardest thing for you to wait for when you were a child in grade school?
   - ❒ Christmas
   - ❒ my birthday
   - ❒ the family vacation
   - ❒ when school would be out
   - ❒ my allowance
   - ❒ other _____

4. When have you, like the people of Israel, waited seemingly forever for God to respond to you from his "mountaintop"?

5. When you feel far from God, what "gods" do you feel most tempted to turn to in order to fill the void in your life?
   - ❒ money and possessions
   - ❒ popularity and pleasing people
   - ❒ power
   - ❒ security and safety
   - ❒ sex and pleasure
   - ❒ alcohol or drugs
   - ❒ fantasy and withdrawal
   - ❒ other _____

6. Imagine you were waiting right now at the foot of a mountain for word from God. What would make it easier for you to wait?
   - ❒ encouragement from others who were waiting
   - ❒ assurance we weren't waiting at the wrong mountain
   - ❒ some little sign from God that he was "up there"
   - ❒ my remembrance of how he freed me from "Egypt" (previous times of need)

7. What do you need to do in order to improve your ability to "wait on God"?
   ❏ not get so easily distracted by the flashy "gods" around me
   ❏ stick with a supportive community
   ❏ remember others who have had to wait
   ❏ other _____

CARING / 15–45 Minutes / All Together

Leader: This course is drawing to a close. Start the decompression with this exercise.

SHARING

Take a few moments and reflect on this passage from Scripture before moving into prayer. In Psalm 40, David expresses the rewards of waiting patiently for God to move, rather than reaching out to other things and people to find fulfillment.

Have one person read the passage aloud (read slowly!). Then go around and let each person share what God has said to them from this passage about their own situation.

> *I waited patiently for the Lord;*
> *he turned to me and heard my cry.*
> *He lifted me out of the slimy pit,*
> *out of the mud and mire;*
> *he set my feet on a rock*
> *and gave me a firm place to stand.*
> *He put a new song in my mouth,*
> *a hymn of praise to our God.*
> *Many will see and fear*
> *and put their trust in the Lord.*
> *Blessed is the man*
> *who makes the Lord his trust,*
> *who does not look to the proud,*
> *to those who turn aside to false gods.*
> *Many, O Lord my God,*
> *are the wonders you have done.*
> *The things you planned for us*
> *no one can recount to you;*
> *were I to speak and tell of them,*
> *they would be too many to declare.*

PRAYER

Now move into a time of prayer, remembering what others have shared regarding their struggles in waiting on God. If you would like to pray in silence, say the word "Amen" when you have finished your prayer, so the next person will know when to start.

SESSION 12

Ministered to by Angels

| LIFE STORIES | BIBLE STUDY |

PURPOSE

To introduce the issue of "Ministered to by Angels" and to share your appreciation for each other.

AGENDA

 Gathering   Study   Caring

OPEN

 GATHERING / 15 Minutes / All Together

Leader: Welcome any newcomers. Keep in mind that this is the last session or the next to the last session in this course. If you are using the short course, be sure to save some time for the group evaluation at the close of the session. You will find this on pages 75–76.

If you have one more session, take some time at the close of this session to plan a celebration at the end of the next session.

INTRODUCTION

When we go through spiritually dry times, what we thirst for more than anything is God. But we shouldn't forget that God often comes to us in the form of his messengers—people and angels who often appear like people. Opening oneself to God then means opening oneself more to people. That means receiving what they have to give. But it also means contributing ourselves to a giving community. By helping to build a giving community through the discipline of service, we build the kind of community in which we can more regularly encounter God through each other. An old anonymous poem says it well:

> "I sought my soul,
>   But my soul I could not see;
> I sought my God,
>   But my God eluded me;
> I sought my brother,
>   And I found all three."

We will have two sessions on the role of service in building a community in which God can be found, and this is the first. In this session, the emphasis will be on sharing your own story. If you wish to spend another session on this topic and go deeper into this issue, you can choose to move to Track 2 for your final session.

To get started, begin with the Ice-Breaker on the next page.

Ice-Breaker: The Lottery. Congratulations! You just won the lottery—for $1,000,000. Now, what are you going to do with your money?

Below is a list of items to spend your money. In silence, look over the list and select five or six items—and jot down how much you are willing to spend on each item. Remember you only have $1,000,000 total. When you have finished shopping, break the silence and let everyone explain how they spent their money.

$ _____ my own commuter lane on the expressway

$ _____ life-time job guarantee

$ _____ one year of no hassles with my kids

$ _____ success in my career

$ _____ lifetime membership in an Aspen ski club

$ _____ protection against losing my hair as I age

$ _____ spiritual fulfillment

$ _____ non-fattening, endless supply of chocolate

$ _____ condo in Hawaii on the beach

$ _____ trim body, sex appeal, with no work

$ _____ six months off paid vacation

 STUDY / 30 Minutes / Groups of 4

Leader: If you have more than 7 in your group, divide into groups of 4 where everyone can participate. If this is the last session in this course (if you are using the reduced schedule) save time at the close to evaluate this course, using the questions on pages 75–76.

Life Stories. Have someone read aloud the stories of the two people below. Then, use the questions to share some of your own experience.

Art

Art had always considered himself an agnostic. When in the presence of someone he trusted he would admit that he had a yearning for a spiritual connection, but he despaired of ever being able to know God. Nothing irritated him more than zealous churchgoers who would engage him in theological debate, trying to "save" him. Then one day a young couple moved in next door to his apartment. He knew they went to church each Sunday, and one time they even asked him to go with them, but in a non-pushy manner that did not offend him. When he got sick, they came by with a pot of soup. When his mother died, they came by to listen and offer their condolences. On Christmas day they knew he was alone, and they invited him over to spend the day with them. Finally, one Sunday morning as they headed out the door to church, he was at his door waiting to join them. Art found others in this couple's church who had a similar caring lifestyle. He began to feel more and more that this was the way he wanted to live. He still didn't know if he would ever find God. But he felt that if he did, it would be in this kind of church.

Lynette

Lynette had gone to church all of her life, but lately she had come to the conclusion that her spiritual life had settled into a rut. She couldn't blame it on her pastor, because she felt he gave really good sermons. Her church was large enough that she could choose about any kind of Sunday School or home group that she wanted, so she wasn't lacking in learning opportunities. But still something was missing. Then one day a friend invited her to go with her to visit children in a cancer ward. At first she thought it would be too depressing, but with some encouragement from her friend she decided to go anyway. As she met them, she was astounded by the spirit and the faith of many of the children. One 10-year-old boy with cancer that was expected to be terminal sat and talked to her for over a half-hour of what he was expecting heaven to be like. Lynette wasn't sure if it was because of what she gave to them or because of what they gave to her, but she left that ward feeling much closer to God than she had in a long time.

DISCUSS

Questions:

1. Why do you think that Art was able to respond to this young couple next door when he had been resistant to the witness of others?

2. What acts of love and caring by others were an important part of your early spiritual development?

"Nobody is too good for the meanest service. One who worries about the loss of time that such petty, outward acts of helpfulness entail is usually taking the importance of his own career too solemnly."
—Dietrich Bonhoeffer

3. When have you, like Lynette, felt especially close to God after sharing in some way with another human being?

4. How do you react to the idea (such as is presented in the poem in the Introduction) that we often find God through reaching out to serve people?
   ❏ "The more people I meet, the more I like my dog!"
   ❏ Seeing how people behave makes me *more cynical* about God.
   ❏ I don't have time to go to church *and* serve others.
   ❏ I see the need, but I don't know how to help.
   ❏ This needs to be a focus of my spiritual growing.
   ❏ I'm already finding God through this kind of service!

5. What areas of serving others would you be most interested in? (choose as many as apply)
    ❏ volunteering in a hospital
    ❏ little acts of caring for neighbors
    ❏ visiting shut-ins and the elderly
    ❏ building homes for the homeless
    ❏ being a "big brother/sister"
    ❏ welcoming new residents
    ❏ tutoring kids behind in school
    ❏ helping immigrants learn English
    ❏ teaching the illiterate to read
    ❏ working with the dying through hospice
    ❏ cleaning up the environment
    ❏ coaching little league
    ❏ going on a short-term mission to another country or culture
    ❏ helping with a youth camp
    ❏ other _____

6. What would be the biggest hurdle keeping you from doing more to serve others?
    ❏ lack of time
    ❏ lack of the nerve or commitment
    ❏ lack of helping skills
    ❏ lack of support from others
    ❏ nothing!

CARING / 15–45 Minutes / All Together

Leader: Regather everyone back together. If this is the last session, use the evaluation on pages 75–76 to evaluate the course. If you have one more session, use some of the time to plan a party for the close of the last session. If this is your final session, you may want to follow the Caring activities in Session 13.

AFFIRMATION

Every Christian reflects the character of Jesus in some way. As your group has gotten to know each other, you can begin to see how each person demonstrates Christ in their very own personality.

Ask one person to sit in silence while the others share one way in which this person reminds you of Jesus. Then, go around again on the next person, etc.

You remind me of ...

☐ JESUS THE HEALER: You seem to be able to touch someone's life and bind their wounds and help make them whole.

☐ JESUS THE SERVANT: There seems to be nothing that you wouldn't do for someone.

☐ JESUS THE PREACHER: You have a way of sharing your faith that is provoking, inspiring and full of hope.

☐ JESUS THE ADMINISTRATOR: As Jesus had a plan for the disciples, you are able to organize to accomplish great things for God.

☐ JESUS THE REBEL: By doing the unexpected you remind me of Jesus' way of revealing God in unique, surprising ways.

☐ JESUS THE TEACHER: You have a way of bringing the Scripture to life in a way that offers hope and truth.

☐ JESUS THE CRITIC: You have the courage to say what needs to be said, even if it isn't always popular.

☐ JESUS THE LEADER: Because you are a visionary, people would be willing to follow you anywhere.

☐ JESUS THE SACRIFICE: Like Jesus, you seem to be willing to sacrifice anything to glorify God.

☐ JESUS THE MIRACLE WORKER: You seem to defy the laws of nature in your efforts to make God's kingdom come alive.

PRAYER   Close with a time of prayer, asking for God's help in our continued healing and in our commitment to celebrate life.

Ministered to by Angels

LIFE STORIES

BIBLE STUDY

PURPOSE

To finish this course, to celebrate what you have experienced together, and to decide about the future.

AGENDA

 Gathering   Study   Caring

OPEN

GATHERING / 15 Minutes / All Together

Leader: Work backwards on the meeting plan. Decide how much time you need for the group evaluation at the close. Then, set aside time for the Study. The remaining time you can spend in this meaningful and affirming Gathering time.

Tell-Tale Fairy Tales. Let one person answer one or both of the questions below. Then, go to the next person around the group.

1. Which of the following myths or fairy tales best expresses what has happened to you since this group began?
   - ❏ Sleeping Beauty—This group has awakened a beauty in me.
   - ❏ Cinderella—It's been great, but now it's midnight ...
   - ❏ Humpty-Dumpty—"All the King's horses and all the King's men (or women!) couldn't have put me together again."
   - ❏ The Wizard of Oz—We've been to Oz together and found all the love and courage and knowledge we needed.
   - ❏ Pandora's Box—I fear we have just opened it!
   - ❏ Pinocchio—The group has helped me confront my lies.
   - ❏ Peter Pan—I can fly! I can fly!

2. What part of this "fairy-tale" would you most want to "re-read" or re-experience?

STUDY / 30 Minutes / Groups of 4

Leader: Break into groups of 4 if you have more than 7 in your group. Be sure to save the last 15–45 minutes for the evaluation at the close of this meeting.

INTRODUCTION

Jesus' Desert Experience. Before Jesus went out to teach and minister, he faced his own desert experience. He voluntarily went out alone into the desert to meditate on himself and his role in God's plan. It was doubtlessly a time of struggle for him, and we are told he was tempted in many ways. He is tempted to focus his power on serving himself and Satan, but his response in this story, as well as through the actions of the rest of his life, was to commit himself to serving God and God's children.

Have someone in your group read the passage out loud. Then go around on the first question and let everyone speak up. Then go around again on the next question, etc.

4 *Then Jesus was led by the Spirit into the desert to be tempted by the devil. ²After fasting forty days and forty nights, he was hungry. ³The tempter came to him and said, "If you are the Son of God, tell these stones to become bread."*

⁴Jesus answered, "It is written: 'Man does not live on bread alone, but on every word that comes from the mouth of God.' "

⁵Then the devil took him to the holy city and had him stand on the highest point of the temple. ⁶"If you are the Son of God," he said, "throw yourself down. For it is written:

" 'He will command his angels concerning you,
and they will lift you up in their hands,
so that you will not strike
your foot against a stone.' "

⁷Jesus answered him, "It is also written: 'Do not put the Lord your God to the test.' "

⁸Again, the devil took him to a very high mountain and showed him all the kingdoms of the world and their splendor. ⁹"All this I will give you," he said, "if you will bow down and worship me."

¹⁰Jesus said to him, "Away from me, Satan! For it is written: 'Worship the Lord your God, and serve him only.' "

¹¹Then the devil left him, and angels came and attended him.

Matthew 4:1–11

1. Why wouldn't Jesus turn the stones into bread?
   - ❏ Being God, he wasn't really that hungry.
   - ❏ He didn't want to make life too easy when it's so hard for so many.
   - ❏ It was what Satan wanted him to do.
   - ❏ His power was intended to be used for others.

2. Why would it be tempting for Jesus to throw himself down from the highest point of the Temple?
   - ❒ It would provide a spiritual "high."
   - ❒ It would provide an escape from Satan's badgering.
   - ❒ He could prove how much his heavenly Father loves him.
   - ❒ It would be an attention-getting display of his power—for Satan and everyone else.

3. Which of the tactics Jesus uses in his "desert experience" do you feel is most powerful?
   - ❒ quoting Scripture to refute Satan's claims
   - ❒ appealing to a higher authority
   - ❒ telling Satan to take a hike
   - ❒ opening himself to be ministered to by angels

4. In your own recent experience of spiritual dryness, who have been the "angels" (persons seemingly sent from God) who have ministered to you? What have they said or done that was most helpful?

5. Jesus was given several chances to take an "easy out" from his desert experience. When your spiritual life becomes dry, which of these "easy outs" are you tempted to take?
   - ❒ acting like everything really is wonderful with me
   - ❒ "party hearty" and forget spirituality
   - ❒ go to my doctor for some kind of pill
   - ❒ avoid being alone with myself
   - ❒ other _____

6. Jesus used his desert experience to prepare for a lifetime of serving others. How has your own experience of spiritual dryness helped prepare you to serve other people?
   - ❒ It has helped me know what it is like when others go through such a time.
   - ❒ It has helped me re-evaluate what is truly important in life.
   - ❒ It has reminded me of the importance of serving God and others instead of pursuing my own success and glory.
   - ❒ It has helped me know myself better, which means I can relate better to others.
   - ❒ other _____

CARING / 15–45 Minutes / All Together

Leader: Bring all the groups back together. Evaluate your group experience and decide about the future. Then you may want to plan a special time of prayer to conclude this course.

EVALUATION

Take a few minutes to look back over your experience and reflect. Go around on each point and finish the sentences.

1. What are some specific things you have learned in this group about facing a time of spiritual dryness?

2. Are you thinking or acting any differently because of your involvement in this study? In what way?

3. As I see it, our purpose and goal as a group was to:

4. We achieved our goal(s):
   - ❏ completely
   - ❏ almost completely
   - ❏ somewhat
   - ❏ We blew it.

5. The high point in this course for me has been:
   - ❏ the Scripture exercises
   - ❏ the sharing
   - ❏ discovering myself
   - ❏ the fun of the fellowship
   - ❏ belonging to a real community of love
   - ❏ finding new energy and purpose for my life

6. One of the most significant ways I have grown is:

7. In my opinion, our group functioned:
   - ❏ smoothly, and we grew.
   - ❏ pretty well, but we didn't grow.
   - ❏ It was tough, but we grew.
   - ❏ It was tough, and we didn't grow.

8. The thing I appreciate most about the group as a whole is:

CONTINUATION	Do you want to continue as a group? If so, what do you need to improve? Finish the sentence:

"If I were to suggest one thing we could do to improve our group, it would be ... "

MAKE A COVENANT	A covenant is a promise made to each other in the presence of God. Its purpose is to indicate your intention to make yourselves available to one another for the fulfillment of the purposes you share. In a spirit of prayer, work your way through the following sentences, trying to reach an agreement on each statement pertaining to your ongoing life together. Write out your covenant like a contract, stating your purpose, goals and the ground rules for your group.

1. The purpose of our group will be ... (finish the sentence)

2. Our goals will be:

3. We will meet for _____ weeks, after which we will decide if we wish to continue as a group.

4. We will meet from _____ to _____ and we will strive to start on time and end on time.

5. We will meet at _____ (place) or we will rotate from house to house.

CURRICULUM	If you decide to continue as a group for a few more weeks, what are you going to use for study and discipline? There are several other studies available at this 201 Series level. 301 Courses, designed for deeper Bible study with study notes, are also available.

For more information about small group resources and possible direction, please contact your small group coordinator or SERENDIPITY at 1-800-525-9563.

Studies From the Old Testament

1. Moses and the Burning Bush (Exo. 3:1–15)
    Consider the times God has appeared to you in the midst of the
    common experiences of your journey.

2. Manna and Quail (Exo. 16:1–31)
    Take a look at how God provides for you spiritually.

3. Balaam's Donkey and the Angel (Num. 22:21–35)
    Think of how God has stepped into the path of your life to try to
    correct your direction.

4. Joshua Renews the Covenant (Josh. 24:1–27)
    Explore what it would mean to renew your own relationship with
    God.

5. Solomon's Wealth and Women (1 Kings 10:23–11:6)
    Think through what it is that comes between you and your rela-
    tionship with God.

6. Job Tested (Job 1:1–22)
    Reflect on what puts your faith to the test and how you respond.

7. Three Men in a Fiery Furnace (Dan. 3:13–30)
    Consider what challenges your faith would enable you to meet,
    and the role of prayer in the midst of those challenges.

Studies From the New Testament

1. The Beatitudes (Matt. 5:3–10)
    Consider what basic attitudes make for a blessed life.

2. Jesus Heals a Paralytic (Mark 2:1–12)
    Look at the areas of your life that are "on the injury list" and what
    might be done to heal them.

3. Transfiguration of Jesus (Mark 9:2–13)
    Remember your own "mountaintop" experiences, and what they
    mean for faith after you have "come down" off the mountain.

4. Gethsemane (Mark 14:32–42)
    Take a look at your own struggle for God's direction when spiritu-
    al dryness creates a "Gethsemane" in your life.

5. Jesus' Teaching on Prayer (Luke 11:1–13)
   Learn how following Jesus' teaching on prayer might help you pull out of your spiritually dry times.

6. On the Road to Emmaus (Luke 24:13–35)
   Learn to recognize Jesus' presence alongside you when you are in a spiritual crisis.

7. Jesus Washes His Disciples' Feet (John 13:1–17)
   Think through what it means to serve others and the importance of service in your spiritual life.

RESOURCES FOR FURTHER STUDY

Angelou, Maya. *Wouldn't Take Nothing for My Journey Now* (New York: Bantam Books, 1993).
   • This best-seller contains reflections on the life and philosophy of the popular African-American author.

Buechner, Frederick. *The Sacred Journey* (San Francisco: Harper Collins, 1982).
   • The popular writer of fiction and non-fiction tells his own life story, and the spiritual meanings he has gleaned from his story.

Foster, Richard J. *Celebration of Discipline* (San Francisco: Harper & Row, 1978).
   • This is a contemporary classic which helps us see the importance of the spiritual disciplines historically and in contemporary life.

—————. *Prayer* (San Francisco: Harper Collins, 1992).
   • This is a follow up to Foster's popular *Celebration of Discipline* and focuses on the different kinds and functions of prayer.

L'Engle, Madeleine. *A Circle of Quiet* (New York: Farrar, Straus and Giroux, 1972).
   • This contains some of the popular author's reflections on life, and the role of having a solitary place where one can find "a circle of quiet."

Miller, Keith. *A Second Touch* (Waco, TX: Word Books, 1967).
   • This is a modern Christian classic, which especially speaks to Christians who feel they have lost the zeal they had when they first became a Christian.

Willard, Dallas. *The Spirit of the Disciplines* (San Francisco: Harper & Row, 1988).
  • This book is less a reflection on how to do spiritual disciplines, than an explanation of *why* we need to do them.

Wueller, Flora Slosson. *Prayer, Stress and Our Inner Wounds* (Nashville, TN: The Upper Room, 1985).
  • This book contains some suggested approaches to prayer which can help bring healing from past hurts and present stresses.